SATIS UPDATE 91

Contents

- ■ SATIS resources
- ■ About UPDATE 91
- ■ Cross-references with
  - ○ Science National Curriculum attainment targets
  - ○ Subject areas – biology, chemistry, physics, geography, sixth-form general studies, technology
  - ○ Cross-curricular themes
  - ○ 100 new frontsheets for the Teachers' Notes of units 101 to 1010 linking them to the National Curriculum
- ■ New student pages for the following SATIS units (interleaved with the teachers' pages)

First Published 1991 by the Association for Science Education.

© 1991 The Association for Science Education

The Association for Science Education
College Lane, Hatfield, Herts AL10 9AA

ISBN 0 86357 139 5

Produced by Communications Management International

SATIS resources

The Update book refers to a range of resources linked with the SATIS Project.

Material for students aged 14 to 16 (or 17)

SATIS units
Copyright-waived material for photocopying

SATIS 1 to 7   (published 1986)
SATIS 8 to 10   (published 1988)
SATIS 11 and 12   (published 1991)
General Guide for Teachers (published 1986)

SATIS topics 14–16
Audio tapes

A series of 24 topics, each lasting 7 minutes or so, which were originally broadcast by BBC Schools Radio in 1989–90. They were devised to support and enhance SATIS printed material. These programmes are now available on C-60 audio cassettes from the ASE.

109	Nuclear Power
206	Test-tube Babies
207	The Story of Fritz Haber
302	Living with Kidney Failure
304	A Medicine to Control Bilharzia
307	Chemicals from Salt
309	Microbes make Human Insulin
402	DDT and Malaria
406	Blindness
407	Noise
409	Dam Problems
502	The Coal Mine Project
504	How Safe is Your Car?
601	Electricity on Demand
602	The Limestone Inquiry
603	The Heart Pacemaker
607	Scale and Scum
801	The Water Pollution Mystery
802	Hypothermia
806	Stress
807	Radiation – how much do you get?
903	What are the Sounds of Music?
907	Your Stars – revelation or reassurance?
1010	Can it be done? Should it be done?

Teachers' programme

SATIS Audiovisual
Tape-slide programmes

1 *Acid from the air* – a programme about acid rain
2 *More wheat for better bread* – a programme about the impact of science and technology on agriculture
3 *More and more people* – a programme about human population growth
4 *Dams, people and the environment* – a programme about the environmental effects of dams
5 *Radiation around us* – a programme about low-level radiation
6 *Bridges* – a programme about the design and construction of bridges

The SATIS Atlas
The SATIS Atlas will comprise a set of copyright-waived maps giving information and data linked to the science curriculum accompanied by associated questions. It will be published in January 1992.

Material for students aged 16 to 19

SATIS 16–19 units
Copyright-waived material for photocopying
This is a set of resources for students in sixth forms and further education. It comprises five files each containing 25 units. Three files were published in 1990 and more material is due for publication in 1991.

Readers
Three booklets, *What is Science?*, *What is Technology?* and *How does Society Decide?* due for publication in 1991.

SATIS topics 16–19
Audio tapes similar to those for SATIS 14–16

Slide set
Sixty colour slides with notes to support selected units in the first three files.

Material for students aged 8 to 14

A project for students in primary and lower secondary education is under development. Material will become available in 1992.

SATIS developments

The latest ideas, together with information about the SATIS Projects and user groups will be published at regular intervals in *Education in Science*, a publication sent to members of the Association for Science Education.

SATIS materials are available from
ASE Booksales,
The Association for Science Education,
College Lane, Hatfield, Herts AL10 9AA
Tel. 0707 267411   Fax 0707 266532

Using NERIS Information service

Update 91 provides search terms for NERIS (The National Educational Resources Information Service). This is a curriculum information service for schools, available either on-line with a computer and modem linked to the telephone system, or as a CD-ROM of the complete data base. (The CD-ROM is updated and replaced every term.)

These services are available on subscription. Full details are available from

NERIS,
Maryland College,
Leighton Street, Woburn MK17 9JD.
Tel. 0525 290364 or Fax 0525 290288

The search terms suggested are based on the *extended system of NERIS on-line* and were tested at the time of publication. They should be taken only as starting points since information is being added to the data base all the time.

The search terms provided in *Update 91* will help you to find information closely linked with the unit – such as worksheets, videos, investigations, project ideas etc.

Here is a typical search. Suppose you wish to use SATIS 210, *The Pesticide Problem*, and would like to know what material related to the unit is available for teachers. If you enter on separate lines

line 1   CO: PESTICIDES
line 2   ME: TEACHER NOTES
line 3   AP: UPPER SECONDARY

the computer will combine the elements for content (CO), media (ME) and age range of pupils (AP) to select the relevant records.

Feedback from teachers

The SATIS project commissioned two evaluation studies in 1987 and 1989 to learn how its material was being used. In all, 1000 schools (both state-maintained and independent) were mailed with questionnaires. The evaluator also visited schools and interviewed both teachers and students.

In addition, there have been less formal feedback paths by which teachers have passed on their experiences of using SATIS materials. SATIS user groups have sprung up, evaluation questionnaires are provided in books SATIS 8, 9 and 10 and the SATIS Team have given numerous presentations and workshops. And of course there has been feedback by word of mouth! In 1989 a fold-and-freepost questionnaire about the revision of SATIS was inserted into *Education in Science* which elicited hundreds of interesting responses.

Update 91 is the result of feedback from teachers – an at-a-glance set of ideas on where in the curriculum the units have been useful and how they may be adapted; whether they need supervision by a science teacher or whether they may be set for independent use or for homework. *Update 91* also suggests links between SATIS materials. Some schools have grouped units together into mini courses, such as those on energy or on medical technology, while others link units with a common learning strategy, like role-play.

Looking to the National Curriculum

As the curriculum changes, so does the need for material. It is time to look again at the diversity of SATIS material. Units less used in the past link strongly with newer topics in the Science National Curriculum. For example, *Computers and Jobs (507)* and *Robots at Work (610)* link with AT 12, *IT and microelectronics*. And there are several units which touch on AT 17, *The nature of science*, perhaps most surprisingly, one about horoscopes which examines the nature of scientific evidence, *Your Stars: Revelation or Reassurance? (907)*.

Key words have been used to indicate the main science content. Although National Curriculum Attainment Targets have been given, units have not been mapped to specific levels. Many units emphasise activities and the social implications of science. It has been found that teachers use these units in very different ways and therefore see different links to National Curriculum statements. On the other hand, there are a large number or units whose content is clearly defined, like *What are the Sounds of Music? (903)* and *Fibre Optics and Telecommunications (306)*. It is hoped that the key words and curriculum links will provide a flexible cue enabling teachers to identify units appropriate to their needs.

Some SATIS units have been widely used in other subject areas such as geography, sixth-form general studies and occasionally with science A-levels. Some provide contexts and design opportunities for the Technology National Curriculum for example, *Hypothermia (802), Bridges (501), The Design Game (106)* and the new unit, *Project Management (1110)*, explains critical path analysis.

Adapting SATIS units

These are suggestions made by SATIS teachers.

□ Pick out the scientific terms before the unit is attempted. Producing a glossary may overcome the difficulties posed by a few unfamiliar words. (Dictionaries may be as helpful as old-fashioned science textbooks for this purpose.) The frontsheets in *Update 91* contain some suggestions.

☐ In some circumstances, students may usefully make their own glossaries – as a revision exercise or to assist them with another reading of the text. Such glossaries may include definitions, popular meanings, examples etc.

☐ Making the language simple for the less able. Teachers have produced alternative pages (keeping the illustrations) often in a worksheet format.

☐ Add more active learning strategies – discussions, role-plays, group work etc. For example in *Materials for Life (506)*, question 5 could be acted out, with students taking the parts of the doctor, Kim and Kim's parents.

☐ Adding extra interest with a video, slide set or using other written material.

☐ Extending the unit for the more able. Projects, holiday work, research suggestions, 'look-around-you' tasks have been used according to resources and circumstances.

☐ Restructuring the unit or omitting sections to fit the time available.

The pages in *Update 91* give specific examples.

SATIS and homework

There are many opportunities for students to use SATIS units at home and this has been suggested by phrases like 'homework possible'. There are usually three contexts in which homework is appropriate.

☐ Some units or parts of units may be used by students working on their own, for example, *High Pressure Chemistry (810)* or Part 1 of *How Safe is Your Car? (504)*.

☐ Some units require student preparation before a class activity. For example, students may be given briefings for discussions or role-plays to prepare at home, such as *The Limestone Inquiry (602)*. Frequently there is information to be read before a discussion or experiment, such as in *Electric Vehicles (202)*. Some units like *Electricity in Your Home (701)* require home surveys – teachers may need to approach these with sensitivity as they may impinge on family matters.

☐ Homework may be used as a follow-up to a unit – for example, writing a report, doing a data-management exercise, for example, *The Water Pollution Mystery (801)*, or *Prospecting by Chemistry (1203)*.

Experience suggests that the open nature of many SATIS questions and activities can produce quantities of marking. The use of group work and oral discussion provides students with immediate feedback from fellow students and permits the teacher to intervene as necessary. These strategies can reduce the marking load considerably. Many teachers have devised schemes to keep the marking to a minimum. Books 11 and 12 provide complete answers which could be referred to by students themselves.

SATIS and active learning

SATIS materials encourage students to participate in the learning process. *The General Guide for Teachers* provides many hints for handling active learning approaches.

SATIS aims to heighten students' awareness of the place of science and technology in their lives. Some units raise sensitive and controversial issues. For such topics, it is important that students have the opportunity to reflect, share and evaluate their understanding and opinions. Discussion and role-play provide useful approaches.

Many SATIS units contain material suitable for small group discussion, although the questions posed may also be answered on paper. Discussion may be followed by group presentations and personal writing and reporting.

Small group discussion

Managing small group discussion will largely depend on the degree of structure provided in the group task.

Highly structured tasks need little teacher direction simply because the guidelines are given in the task itself – for example SATIS units *Living with Kidney Failure (302)* and *Nuclear Power (109)*. Similarly, so do tasks which involve practical work, problem solving or decision making where there is an end product, such as *Food from Fungus (102)* or where group members have particular roles to carry out in the task such as *Paying for National Health (503)*.

Less structured tasks involving ideas or issues but leading the pupils in a particular direction can be more productive if students build an agenda with the help of the questions in the text and proceed with step-by-step discussion, for example *Materials for Life (506)*, *AIDS (909)* and *Tin Cans (1106)*.

The teacher's role is to ensure that reflective discussion takes place to:

☐ clarify the points made

☐ summarise and consolidate

☐ share each group's views

☐ ensure whole class discussion

□ allow individuals to gain in confidence by speaking to the whole class after 'rehearsing' in their small group.

Discussion activities may include group presentations to the whole class. It is important to allow students time for preparation and rehearsal in a small group beforehand.

Role-play

A few SATIS units are designed for role-play, regarded by many of us as one of the most difficult active learning strategies to run successfully.

Before embarking on large scale role-plays, it is helpful to know if your students use role-play in other subject areas. And, if some have special talent in improvisation and drama, they may be able to lend support to the less confident.

Short 'mini' role-plays, carried out in pairs or small groups help to build up students' confidence in taking on roles without an 'audience'. The new units, *Breast or Bottle (1101)*, *A Special Type of Hearing Aid (1102)* and *Telephones (1108)* provide a range of scenarios.

Small group role-plays provide practice before students move on towards more complex and demanding situations. *Dam Problems (409)*, involves groups of eight or nine students. *Quintonal (1002)* can be used very flexibly.

A few SATIS units involve the whole class together in a role-play. Often this is a simulation of a public inquiry or meeting, for example *The Limestone Inquiry (602)*, *The Coal Mine Project (502)* and *Should we Build a Fallout Shelter? (608)*.

The short BBC Radio programme, *The Coal Mine Project*, (from SATIS Topics 14–16) eavesdrops on students doing the unit. It provides an excellent example of preparing for role-play which is worth listening to before undertaking any role-play for the first time.

Role-play can be thought of as taking place in five stages:

1 Preparation
SATIS units supply background information in the general briefings. Some of the BBC Radio programmes provide additional material to set the scene, like *Dam Problems* and *The Limestone Inquiry*. If the briefing is long, it can help to record it on cassette for students to listen to.

The teacher needs to make students aware of the procedure, have clear aims, create enthusiasm and assign roles carefully, allowing time for preparation.

2 Getting into role
SATIS provides students with role-play cards or briefings.

Some roles are better tackled by students in groups of two or three, such as the inspectors in the *Limestone Inquiry (602)* or the roles in *Should we Build a Fallout Shelter? (608)*. Teachers have been successful with either two or three students appearing in a single role, or with one acting as spokesperson and the others as consultants.

The following are suggestions to help students internalise their roles:

□ rewriting the brief in the first person ('I feel .... I think .... etc.')

□ providing questions on the back of the role-play card to develop the character. (The example given here is for *Quintonal: an industrial hazard (1002)*.)

□ taking on these characters and interviewing each other (e.g. reporter interviews character), before the proper role-play begins.

3 Running the action
Create an appropriate 'atmosphere'. Let students use props. Make sure they understand their briefings, then hand over responsibility to the students, intervening only in-role.

4 Debriefing
This is to establish the facts and decisions agreed upon; to review feelings, behaviour or actions. The process may be started with discussion in small groups and shared with the whole class later.

5 Follow-up
Relate the classroom experience to real-life situations; establish its usefulness in developing pupils' understanding of issue; explore further study or information required; identify links with continuing studies.

The above suggestions for discussion and role-play have been adapted from the 'ATLAS Teachers Support Manual' to be published in 1991 by Unwin Hyman as part of the ATLAS project. The book describes a range of active learning strategies, and develops further those used in SATIS, with specific chapters devoted to each one.

List of units in the SATIS 14–16 series

Science National Curriculum attainment targets

The following list suggests how SATIS units may be linked with the attainment targets of the Science National Curriculum. Many units link with several attainment targets. The brackets indicate links with only a minor part of that unit.

AT 1	Exploration of science	110 201 205 208 209 210 405 505 509 606 706 709 801 807 809 904 907 910 1001 1004 1007 1008 1009 1101 1103 1104 1105ab 1106 1110 1201 1203 1205 1208
AT 2	The variety of life	102 201 (208) 210 304 402 404 505 (703) 906 1004 1009 1201
AT 3	Processes of life	102 104 108 110 (201) 203 206 208 302 (304) 309 401 402 503 506 508 509 603 606 (608) (609) 703 707 802 (803) 805 806 901 909 1002 (1005) 1101 1204 1210
AT 4	Genetics and evolution	309 807 901 (1004) (1103) 1202 1204
AT 5	Human influences on the Earth	301 304 308 310 401 402 404 409 410 502 602 605 (607) 708 801 803 902 1001 1103 1106 1201 1203 1210
AT 6	Types and uses of materials	101 (405) 408 410 506 604 (910) 1104 1106
AT 7	Making new materials	102 103 105 207 (305) 307 310 405 502 505 510 604 (607) 709 810 (904) 1001 1003 1004 1103 1106 1204
AT 8	Explaining how materials behave	(109) 204 205 (305) 608 807 808 (1004) 1105ab
AT 9	Earth and atmosphere	(602) 1107 1205 1206
AT 10	Forces	501 504 705 (708) 809 (1006) (1009)
AT 11	Electricity and magnetism	701 704 804 908 1007 1008 (1101) 1108 1109 1208
AT 12	IT and microelectronics	306 507 (603) 610 905 906 (1101) 1102 1108 1109 1208
AT 13	Energy	106 107 109 201 202 303 308 403 409 502 504 508 702 704 705 (706) 802 807 808 809 908 (1006) (1101) 1109
AT 14	Sound and music	407 705 903 1102
AT 15	Using light and electromagnetic radiation	209 303 306 406 (704) 1207
AT 16	The Earth in space	1209
AT 17	The nature of science	207 305 (306) 309 509 510 609 805 (810) (901) 907 1108 1202 1204 1208

Subject areas

The following are units with strong links to specific subject areas.

Biology	102 104 108 110 201 203 204 206 208 209 210 301 302 304 305 308 309 401 402 404 406 407 409 503 506 508 509 606 609 703 707 801 802 803 805 806 901 902 906 909 1002 1004 1005 1006 1009 1010 1101 1102 1103 1104 1105a 1201 1202 1204
Chemistry	101 103 105 110 203 204 205 207 210 301 305 307 308 310 401 402 404 405 408 410 502 505 506 510 602 604 607 702 706 709 801 810 902 904 910 1001 1002 1003 1004 1010 1103 1104 1106 1203 1204 1210
Physics	106 107 109 202 204 205 209 303 306 308 403 404 407 501 504 507 508 601 603 608 610 701 702 704 705 706 708 802 803 804 807 808 809 903 905 907 908 1006 1007 1008 1009 1010 1101 1102 1105ab 1106 1108 1109 1207 1208 1209
Geography	106 107 109 110 208 301 304 403 404 409 502 505 602 604 605 708 901 902 1001 1105a 1107 1109 1203 1205 1206
Sixth-form General Studies	102 104 105 106 107 108 109 110 203 204 206 207 208 301 302 308 309 404 405 407 409 502 503 507 508 509 605 607 608 610 703 802 803 806 807 808 901 902 905 906 907 908 909 910 1002 1003 1005 1010 1101 1105a 1109 1110 1202
Technology	102 103 104 106 107 108 201 202 205 208 303 305 306 308 404 405 407 410 501 503 506 507 603 605 610 707 708 802 803 905 906 1006 1010 1101 1103 1106 1110

Cross-curricular themes

Many SATIS units include cross-curricular themes. This list is for general guidance only and was compiled before National Curriculum Council publications were available.

Health Education	102 104 108 203 204 206 208 209 302 304 305 309 401 402 404 406 407 503 506 508 509 603 606 608 609 703 707 708 709 802 803 805 806 807 901 904 909 910 1002 1005 1007 1010 1002 1005 1007 1010 1101 1102 1104 1105a 1202 1210
Environment	101 107 108 201 202 210 301 307 308 402 404 407 409 410 502 505 508 602 605 703 801 803 902 1001 1010 1103 1106 1201 1203 1205 1206
Careers	507 610 905
Citizenship	104 109 203 206 207 302 406 407 409 502 503 504 507 508 602 605 607 608 705 807 905 1002 1003 1005 1106
Economic and Industrial Understanding (listed as 'Economic Awareness' in the text)	102 103 105 106 202 208 210 302 307 310 403 408 503 604 605 610 701 703 704 709 904 905 908 1001 1004 1010 1001 1004 1010 1103 1106 1201 1204 1210

Sulphurcrete

Science content

Melting, crystallization, plasticity, composite material.

Science curriculum links
AT 6   Types and uses of materials

Syllabus links
○   GCSE Science, Chemistry

Cross-curricular themes
○   Environment

Lesson time
  1–2 hours
  (plus homework)

Links with other SATIS materials
902   Acid Rain
1104   Materials to Repair Teeth

NERIS
Search on
   SULPHUR

STUDENT ACTIVITIES

☐ Reading and answering questions: reasons for making sulphurcrete.

☐ Practical work: making sulphur concrete from sulphur and sand.

☐ Reading and answering questions: sulphurcrete as a composite material.

USE

As a demonstration of the properties of sulphur, of composite materials or to show an economic use of a 'waste product'.

Most teachers prefer to demonstrate the making of sulphurcrete.

The unit is better suited to able students and best done in its entirety. Part 1 may be used for homework.

ADAPTING THE UNIT

☐ Some teachers provide students with a question sheet on which to note down their answers while the experiment is demonstrated.

☐ Part 3 has been used for class discussion.

First published 1986

Food from Fungus

Science content

Food production, fermentation in manufacture, diet.

Science curriculum links
AT 2   The variety of life
AT 3   Processes of life
AT 7   Making new materials

Syllabus links
○ GCSE Science, Biology
○ Sixth-form General Studies
○ Technology (Home Economics)

Cross-curricular themes
○ Health Education
○ Economic Awareness

Lesson time
    1½ hours
    (and homework)

Links with other SATIS materials
108   Fibre in your Diet
208   The Price of Food
703   Vegetarianism

STUDENT ACTIVITIES

☐ Reading and answering questions: mycoprotein, manufacture by fermentation, protein comparisons.

☐ Decision-making: a group activity to devise a marketing strategy for mycoprotein.

USE

Extends work on diet and health – suitable for a range of abilities and age groups (third to sixth form). Has been found to link well with Cell Biology and Biotechnology modules.

ADAPTING THE UNIT

☐ Lower ability students need to be talked through the information and shown how it relates to what they have learnt.

☐ For Part 3, if time is limited, designing the poster is the most important activity.

FURTHER INFORMATION

Mycoprotein was first used in convenience foods. It is now marketed as a food in its own right under the name *Quorn*.

At present controlling the environment to grow mycoprotein requires considerable expertise and production costs are fairly high. If the scale of production can be increased then Quorn may turn out to be a low-cost food suitable for the Developing World.

Quorn is suitable for ovo-lacto vegetarians but because it contains a small amount of egg white is not suitable for vegans. It is also suitable for diabetics and coeliacs (people with a gluten intolerance). However, anyone on a special diet should check prepared dishes for other ingredients.

Mycoprotein compared with other sources of protein

	Protein g/100g	Dietary fibre g/100g	Total fats g/100g	Fats ratio PUPA:SFA	Chol-esterol mg/100g	Energy kJ/100g
Mycoprotein	11.8	4.8	3.5	-	-	360
Cheddar cheese	26.0	-	33.5	0.2	70	170
Egg boiled	12.3	-	10.9	0.3	450	615
Chicken boiled	29.2	-	7.3	0.4	80	765
Cod steamed	18.6	-	0.9	2.2	60	345
Haricot beans	6.6	7.4	0.5	-	-	390

First published 1986

Controlling Rust

Science content

Causes of rusting, economic implications, ways of preventing the process.

Science curriculum links
AT 7 Making new materials

Syllabus links
○ GCSE Science, Chemistry
○ Technology

Cross-curricular themes
○ Economic Awareness

Lesson time
1–2 hours
(homework possible)

Links with other SATIS materials
310 Recycling Aluminium
604 Metals as Resources
1106 Tin Cans

NERIS
Search on
RUSTING
or on
CORROSION

STUDENT ACTIVITIES

☐ Reading information and answering questions: cost, causes and prevention of rust.

☐ Decision-making: effectiveness and costing of rust-proofing methods.

☐ Case study: students are given data for interpretation on four ways to protect the school bridge.

☐ Discussion points.

USE

As a summary of practical work on rusting or to revise and extend work on metal protection for both science and technology courses. Individual or group work are both possible throughout the unit. Suitable for middle and upper abilities.

Part 3, protecting the school bridge, is particularly popular and should not be omitted! It is suitable for homework.

ADAPTING THE UNIT

☐ Lower ability students may find the maths on page 5 demanding. See the blue Teachers' Notes.

FURTHER INFORMATION

The cost of rust is said to be 3.5% of the Gross National Product (GNP). In 1988 the GNP was £4.7 × 10^{11}, giving a figure for the cost of rust of £16,000 million.

OTHER RESOURCES

The booklet in the Teachers' Notes called *Corrosion and Protection of Metals – Information for use by teachers*, is still available free of charge. The slides cost £20 + VAT.

Available from the National Corrosion Service, Tel. 081- 943 7113.

The Keep Britain Tidy metals unit has been helpful. Contact The Education Officer, The Tidy Britain Group, The Pier, Wigan WN3 4EX.

First published 1986

What's in our Food?

Science content

Food processing, nutritional information, additives.

Science curriculum links
AT 3 Processes of life

Syllabus links
○ GCSE Science, Biology
○ Sixth-form General Studies
○ Technology (Home Economics)

Cross-curricular themes
○ Health Education
○ Citizenship

Lesson time
1–2 hours
(and homework)

Links with other SATIS materials
102 Food from Fungus
208 The Price of Food
703 Vegetarianism

NERIS
Search on
FOOD ADDITIVES

STUDENT ACTIVITIES

☐ Survey, a data gathering exercise: looking at food labels at home.

☐ Survey: extension into food additives.

☐ Discussion points for small group work: do we need food additives?

Students are provided with a food label factsheet.

USE

To link with work on food and food preservation. This is a very popular unit which has been used within the fourth and occasionally by third years.

The factsheets, pages 4 and 5, should be stapled separately for convenience of use.

Tables 1, 2 and 3 require a positive response from teachers and there is a large amount of marking involved.

ADAPTING THE UNIT

☐ To shorten the unit, focus either on *nutrition* (Table 2) or on food processing (Table 1), extending either topic if time permits into *food additives* (Table 3) and the *discussion*.

☐ Collect food labels from other countries (on a school trip or for a holiday task). It is useful to compare labels for products which are also available in the UK, for example, milk, packet soups or soft drinks like Fanta and Coca-Cola.

☐ Use the unit to suggest diets for students suffering from various disorders, for example no milk (lactophobic), no gluten (coeliac). Major stores like Tesco, J Sainsbury and Gateway will provide lists of foods for these people.

FURTHER INFORMATION

☐ Food labelling in the UK is voluntary. The Government published a set of guidelines in 1988.

☐ The Government intends to permit the sale of food treated by gamma irradiation. This food will be clearly labelled. Some European Countries already allow irradiation and there are draft EC proposals to permit it within the Community.

First published 1986

The Bigger the Better?

Science content

Chemicals made from oil, breaking up and joining molecules.

Science curriculum links
AT 7   Making new materials

Syllabus links
○ GCSE Science, Chemistry
○ Sixth-form General Studies
○ A-level Chemistry

Cross-curricular themes
○ Economic Awareness

Lesson time
   1–2 hours
   (homework possible)

NERIS
Search on
      ETHENE
or on
      CRACKING (PETROLEUM)

STUDENT ACTIVITIES

☐ Reading, data handling and answering questions: a comparative study of costing different sized crackers.

☐ Questions: the problems associated with large industrial plants.

☐ Group discussion questions: economies of scale in other industries.

USE

As part of a study of how chemicals are made from oil. The unit shows the importance of economics for an understanding of how the chemical industry functions.

This is a challenging unit, requiring a high level of mathematical skill, best suited to able fifth formers. The Teachers' Notes suggest giving students the figures, if they find the calculations too demanding.

ADAPTING THE UNIT

☐ To supplement Part 3, arrange a visit to a local factory. Have students prepare a questionnaire beforehand based on the ideas in this unit.

☐ The unit has been used for assessment of data handling skills (upper abilities only).

FURTHER INFORMATION

Since the unit was written capital costs have risen a little, but crude oil and therefore naphtha prices have fallen. Overall the figures illustrate the point well in 1990.

Crackers are not big polluters compared with other petrochemical plants or other industries, but every effort is made to achieve the higher standards which society now requires.

Question 18 page 5 – Saudi Arabia and other oil producing countries have indeed built their own crackers and ethene consuming units.

In Britain, petrochemical companies have reacted by making ethene from North Sea ethane – Exxon and Shell have commissioned the new cracker at Mossmorran in Fifeshire and BP at Grangemouth have announced new production capacity. Ethane is a good raw material when ethene is the only product required.

ICI on Teeside does not have a supply of North Sea ethane, but now uses large quantities of propane as well as naphtha. This produces propene as well as ethene.

First published 1986

The Design Game

Science content

Energy conservation, domestic insulation.

Science curriculum links
AT13 Energy

Syllabus links
- ○ GCSE Science, Physics
- ○ Geography
- ○ Sixth-form General Studies
- ○ Technology

Cross-curricular themes
- ○ Economic Awareness

Lesson time
1–2 hours

Links with other SATIS materials
701   Electricity in your Home
1006   As Safe as Houses

NERIS
Search on
       ENERGY EFFICIENCY and
       HOMES
or on
       HOUSES

STUDENT ACTIVITIES

☐ Reading: information on heat loss from houses, passive solar heating.

☐ Design task and questions: designing an energy-efficient bungalow.

☐ Problem solving: insulation task.

USE

Suitable for any scheme of work which involves energy use in the home. The unit is very popular with teachers and students of all abilities. It has been used mostly with third and fourth years and occasionally with second years.

Some points to watch for: Students tend to 'play house' and can miss the scientific point. Teachers can be left with a mess everywhere when the bell goes. There are too many cut out items and they are fiddly to manage. Dimensions are difficult to judge.

This work in science may be used as a starting point for work in technology where students will be expected to consider design in relation to many factors including anthropometric data.

ADAPTING THE UNIT

☐ Some teachers do not use page 5 – too messy.

☐ Ration the number of items that students may cut out and use – bedroom 3, dining room 2 (omitting chairs), living room 5, bathroom 3, do not fit out the kitchen.

☐ Students could draw in the furniture using the outlines on page 5. However, this does not allow them to experiment.

☐ Students could be encouraged to use the appropriate graphic symbols for windows, doors etc. in their designs.

FURTHER INFORMATION

☐ The scale used on page 5 is 1:50. (It is the same scale as the grid on page 4.) The appliances have standard dimensions, for example: single bed 0.80 m × 1.90 m
double bed 1.50 m × 1.90 m
cooker and refrigerator are both 600 mm × 600 mm
bath 1.70 m × 0.70 m

Students should be able to work out the size of other objects. Doorways are 800 mm wide. They should allow at least 600 mm space for passing behind a chair.

First published 1986

Ashton Island – A problem in renewable energy

Science content

Use of renewable energy sources; solar, geothermal, tidal, energy from biomass, wind and waves.

Science curriculum links
AT13 Energy

Syllabus links
- ○ GCSE Science, Physics
- ○ Geography
- ○ Sixth-form General Studies
- ○ Technology

Cross-curricular themes
- ○ Environment

Lesson time
1 hour (for Part 2)

Links with other SATIS materials
106	The Design Game
201	Energy from Biomass
403	Britain's Energy Sources

Other energy units
109, 508, 601, 808, 902, 908, 1006, 1010 (questions 14, 2, 4, 13, 28)

SATIS 16–19
20	Energising an Indian village
21	Energy from the wind
46	Energy from the waves
63	Biogas

NERIS
Search on
- FUELLESS ENERGY SOURCES and
- UPPER SECONDARY

Additional search terms:
- SOLAR POWER
- WATER POWER
- WIND POWER
- GEOTHERMAL POWER

STUDENT ACTIVITIES

☐ Part 1 Reading information: renewable forms of energy and how they may be harnessed. Comprehension questions are now provided for this section.

☐ Part 2 Problem-solving: harnessing renewable sources of energy on the island. Best tackled by students working together in small groups. An improved map and an alternative scenario (setting up an educational camp) are provided.

☐ Making a presentation: see *Adapting the unit.*

USE

To draw together studies on renewable energy, following prior work or a film.

Allow students to look through the information before the lesson (perhaps for homework with the new comprehension questions) and then to refer back to it as necessary.

The unit is suitable for all abilities, very popular with both students and teachers. Has been successfully used with third years.

ADAPTING THE UNIT

☐ The unit works well, if students discuss the problem in groups and appoint a spokesperson to present their answers to the class, using an OHP transparency of the map.

☐ Change the context to a more student-centred one. (An educational camp scenario is provided overleaf.)

☐ Comprehension questions for weaker students are printed overleaf.

☐ Use the new map.

NEW MATERIAL

Comprehension questions, new scenario and new map.

First published 1986

Questions for pages 1, 2 and 3 of Ashton Island

Q1 How could you use the Sun's energy for heating water?

Q2 Some pocket calculators have no battery. They harness the Sun's energy instead. How is this done?

Suggest how you could run a solar-powered calculator during the hours of darkness.

Q3 In some parts of the world, springs of hot water bubble up out of the ground. What is this source of energy called?

Q4 What sort of sites are most suitable for using tidal power?

Q5 How could you harness wind energy and convert it into electricity?

Q6 How could you get energy from organic rubbish, manure and plants?

Q7 Which sources of renewable energy are best for supplying the following?
(a)   electricity to a large town
(b)   hot water for 20 people

Part 2 Ashton Island

A charitable trust is to set up an educational camp on Ashton Island (Figure 9). Young people will spend up to three months there doing scientific projects, for example, studying its plants, animals and rocks.

The camp will house 30 people in wooden buildings. One will be used as a laboratory.

Your class will be the first to visit the camp – fares paid by the trust. Your project will be to harness the natural resources of the island to provide the camp with energy for cooking, heating, etc.

Your task is to use the information in the unit to decide how to do it. You must order and ship out the equipment that you will need when you arrive. The builders will have to know where to site the camp. You may assume that the camp will be in use for at least 10 years, although it may be left empty for periods of time.

Look at the map and consider where the camp could be placed. Then answer the following questions.

Ashton Island is in the Pacific Ocean and many miles from the mainland (Figure 9).

The island has:

- No oil, coal or natural gas
- Hot weather by day, but cool nights
- Strong winds from the north east
- A mountain with fast-flowing streams
- Forests
- Hot springs

1 *How will you heat the buildings in cold weather?*

2 *How will you provide enough hot water for washing?*

3 *What sources of energy will you use for cooking? Try to suggest two.*

4 *How will the buildings be lit at night?*

5 *The camp will have two electric refrigerators. How will you provide a reliable supply of electricity for them?*

6 *On a copy of the map, mark where you think the camp should be sited and any sources of energy you would use.*

Key

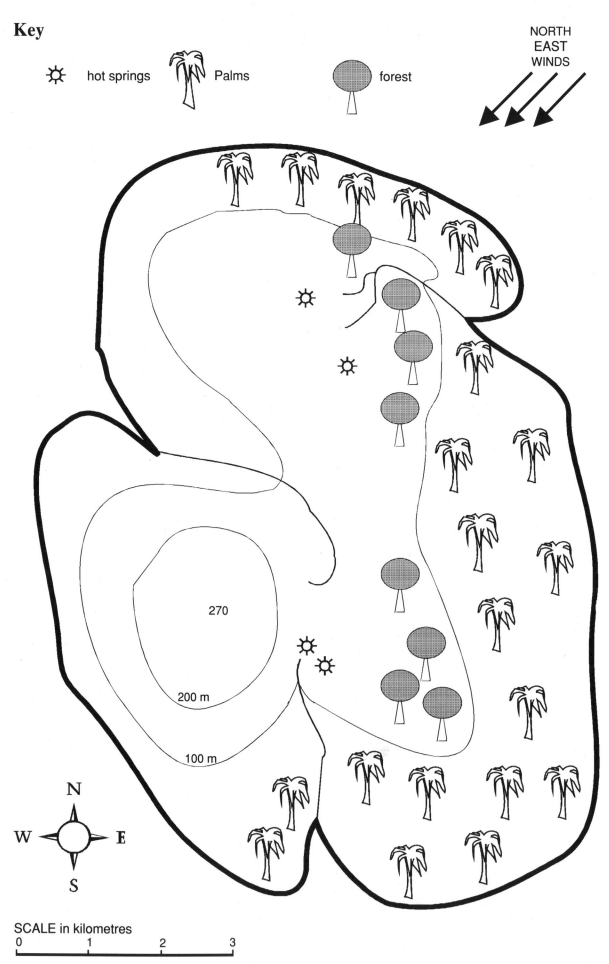

Fibre in your Diet

Science content

Diet and diesase, the human digestive system.

Science curriculum links
AT 3   Processes of life

Syllabus links
○ GCSE Science, Biology
○ Sixth-form General Studies
○ Technology (Home Economics)

Cross-curricular themes
○ Health Education
○ Environment

Lesson time
    1–2 hours

Links with other SATIS materials
102   Food from Fungus
104   What's in our Food?
209   The Price of Food
703   Vegetarianism

NERIS
Search on
    DIETARY FIBRE

STUDENT ACTIVITIES

☐ Reading and answering questions: dietary fibre, the digestive system, diseases involving the gut.

☐ Data search questions: a food values exercise.

☐ Data interpretation and questions: bowel cancer.

USE

Links to work on diet and health and extends to environmental and global implications. Suitable for all abilities and much enjoyed.

It is suggested that page 4, the data sheet, is *not* stapled in with the unit for convenience of use. The questions on page 6 are guides to discussion and are best tackled in small groups.

The original data will become obsolete with the new method of assessing dietary fibre.

FURTHER INFORMATION

Perspectives on the role of 'dietary fibre' have changed significantly and a new method of measurement will be introduced.

'Dietary fibre' is a mixture of substances, mainly non-starch polysaccharides, but also 'resistant starch'. These compounds differ in solubility, their capacity to hold water and ability to be fermented in the large intestine. Each component has a different action in the body. Some shorten the time food lingers in the intestines, which may ease constipation and help prevent bowel cancer, others can in some circumstances reduce cholesterol levels in the blood.

A new method of analysis (Englyst) enables these components to be more accurately measured. Under the new classification most of the components belong to the non-starch polysaccharide (NSP) group – all those polysaccharides except starch.

Current dietary guidelines recommend that fibre intakes should be increased to 18 g of NSP, whereas it was 30 g by the method of assessment used for the data in Table 1. This older data included lignin (which is not a carbohydrate). Figures obtained by the Englyst method do not. This leads to 'lower' values for dietary fibre.

Teachers are recommended to use new figures for dietary fibre based on NSP when a complete set becomes available.

NEW MATERIAL

A rewritten page 1.

First published 1986

FIBRE IN YOUR DIET

A hundred years ago in Britain, only six babies out of ten survived to become adults. Life expectancy was 48 years for a girl and 44 years for a boy.

Improved living conditions and modern medicine have helped wipe out most of the 'killer diseases' like typhoid, smallpox and tuberculosis in Britain. Death in the 1990s is likely to be from one of the 'diseases of modern society', such as heart disease and cancer. Diet may have a role to play in the cause of these diseases. One factor which has attracted a great deal of attention is the amount of 'fibre' in the diet.

Part 1 What is dietary fibre?

Dietary fibre is the term given to a group of substances, mainly complex carbohydrates from plant cell walls, which cannot be digested in the small intestine of human beings. They pass into the colon where some are fermented by bacteria. The table in Part 3 gives the amounts of fibre in different foods.

Read through the information in Parts 1 and 2.

● *Find all the words in pages 1 to 3 which relate to*
(a)   foods
(b)   parts of the body
(c)   diseases
and make a list of them.

● *What do the following words or phrases in the unit mean?*
(a)   life expectancy
(b)   diseases of modern society
(c)   dietary fibre
(d)   faeces
(f)   carcinogens

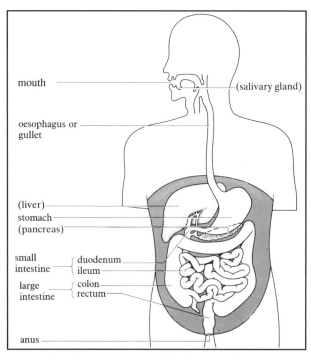

Figure 1 The main parts of the human digestive system

Figure 1 shows the main parts of the human digestive system. As food passes along the gut, it is broken down and absorbed into the bloodstream. By the time it reaches the colon, what is left is mainly fibre. It passes out in the faeces, which also contain water and many millions of bacteria.

People who eat a lot of 'fibre' produce more faeces than people who do not. People in developing countries eating a high fibre, mostly vegetarian diet produce, on average, 300–500 grams of faeces daily. In developed Western countries where the diet contains less fibre, only 80–120 grams of faeces are produced daily. What is more, with the high fibre diet, it only takes about 30 hours for food to pass through the gut from mouth to anus. A typical Western diet low in fibre may take 70 hours to pass through the gut.

Nuclear Power

Science content

Nuclear fuels, radioactivity and nuclear fission.

Science curriculum links
AT8   Explaining how materials behave
AT13 Energy

Syllabus links
○   GCSE Science, Physics
○   Geography
○   Sixth-form General Studies

Cross-curricular themes
○   Citizenship

Lesson time
1–2 hours
(plus preparation)

Links with other SATIS materials
204   Using Radioactivity
807   Radiation – how much do you get?
808   Nuclear Fusion
1010 Can it be done?
      (questions 13, 37, 42)

BBC Radio SATIS Topics 14–16
Nuclear Power

NERIS
Search on
      NUCLEAR POWER and
      UPPER SECONDARY
or on
      ENERGY SOURCES and
      UPPER SECONDARY

STUDENT ACTIVITIES

☐ Reading: nuclear power, nuclear fission, moderators, uranium isotopes.

☐ Test: on nuclear fission.

☐ Preparation for structured discussion (homework): chairperson and four expert briefings.

☐ Discussion points.

USE

To follow work on radioactivity.

This is a difficult unit, suitable for high ability students or for sixth formers.

ADAPTING THE UNIT

☐ Many teachers use only the general briefing and the test.

☐ May be done as a whole class discussion with groups of students using the expert briefings.

☐ The BBC radio programme, 'Nuclear Power', provides background information and talks to representatives from Nirex (the nuclear waste disposal authority) and Greenpeace. It is best used after students have worked through the general briefing and the test.

NEW MATERIAL

A replacement page for EB4·1.

First published 1986

Nuclear Power: Expert's Briefing Sheet 4

Britain's energy sources

You will be taking part in a group discussion on nuclear power. You are the only person in the group who has read this sheet, so you will be the expert on Britain's energy sources.

After you have read this, the Chairperson of your group will be asking the kind of questions an ordinary person would ask. Try to answer them as simply as possible. Draw diagrams if it helps your answers.

Briefing

Britain is fortunate where energy is concerned. Coal, oil and natural gas are all found in Britain, or under the sea around the British Isles. The graph in Figure 1 shows the changes in use of Britain's energy sources since 1950.

energy used (million tonnes of coal equivalent)

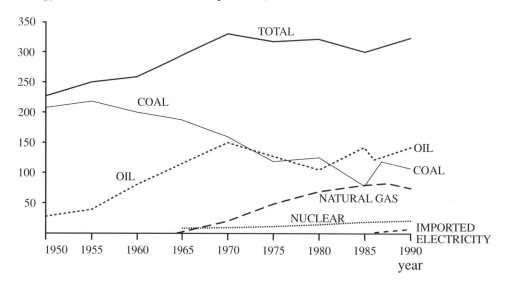

Figure 1 Britain's energy sources

Table 1 Sources of energy used for electricity generation in 1989

Coal	Oil	Nuclear	Hydroelectric	(Electricity from France)
62%	7%	19%	2%	(4 %)

Since 1986, Britain has been able to import electricity cheaply by cable under the Channel from France. In the 1970s with few energy reserves of its own, the French government decided to build a large number of nuclear power stations. By 1995, 75 per cent of France's electricity will be nuclear generated. France now exports electricity to other countries in Europe.

Nuclear power stations are expensive to build and close down when they are old but the cost of running them is relatively low.

Hilltop – an agricultural problem

Science content

Minerals for healthy growth, trace elements in the soil.

Science curriculum links
AT 1 Exploration of science
AT 3 Processes of life

Syllabus links
○ GCSE Science, Biology, Chemistry
○ Geography
○ Sixth-form General Studies

Lesson time
   1 hour

Links with other SATIS materials
401   Fluoridation of Water Supplies
801   The Water Pollution Mystery
1203   Prospecting by Chemistry

STUDENT ACTIVITIES

☐ Reading, data handling, data analysis and answering questions: a cattle farming problem – trace elements, poor health, geological evidence.

USE

As an example of problem-solving in the environment in conjunction with work on plant and animal nutrition.

The unit needs to be used in its entirety. It has a clear end point for students. Page 4 looks more formidable than it is.

'A good space-filler if the top set has got ahead.' 'I used it for the less able'. 'Used for assessment.'

ADAPTING THE UNIT

☐ Make OHP masters of the two maps so that they may be superimposed.

☐ Students are likely to find page 4 easier if they have looked at similar data before. SATIS unit 1203, *Prospecting by Chemistry*, provides an introduction to the ideas used here.

First published 1986

Energy from Biomass

STUDENT ACTIVITIES

☐ Reading and answering questions on:
  - photosynthesis,
  - solid biomass fuels (wood, charcoal, waste straw),
  - liquid biomass fuels (alcohol, oil, gasohol); biogas, oil,
  - biogas – the biogas digestor.

☐ Practical work: 'Build your own biogas digestor'. (This has caused some problems – see below.)

USE

As extension work on energy, fuels and ecology. Suitable for most abilities – popular with students.

Building a biogas digestor is the climax! However, some schools have reported that the experiment often does not work and some girls have refused to do it.

Many teachers ask students to produce the design only. If the experiment is carried out, positive teaching about the hygiene precautions is of real educational value.

Safety note Use manure from herbivorous animals such as cows or horses. (It is unlikely to contain organisms that are really harmful to humans.) Adhere to hygiene procedures – see Chapter 4 of the ASE's *Topics in Safety* second edition (1988).

If students follow the illustrations there should be no problems, but they may well come up with other designs.

Teachers need to be aware that large (dustbin size) volumes of gas present an explosion risk which in some ways is a greater hazard than the microbiological one.

'Only one biogas digestor didn't work!'

ADAPTING THE UNIT

☐ Parts of the unit may be selected for use.
☐ Some teachers add more references to developing countries.
☐ 'Given as holiday work'.
☐ The biogas digestor could be used as a practical investigation.

FURTHER INFORMATION

A 1 megawatt power station using the gas evolved from a landfill site is already operating in Britain. More are planned.

First published 1986

Electric Vehicles

Science content

Kinetic energy, battery, 'stored energy', fuel, efficiency of energy transfer, power, kWh, pollution.

Science curriculum links
AT13 Energy

Syllabus links
- ○ GCSE Science, Physics
- ○ Technology

Cross-curricular themes
- ○ Environment
- ○ Economic Awareness

Lesson time
1–1½ hours
(homework possible)

Links with other SATIS materials
706 Dry Cells
902 Acid Rain

NERIS
Search on
ELECTRIC VEHICLES

STUDENT ACTIVITIES

☐ Reading and questions: electric vehicles – their advantages, energy for motion, how they work, how they compare with petrol vehicles, efficiency, range, recharging, cost, pollution.

☐ Questions for discussion: to consider the advantages and disadvantages of different types of electric vehicle.

USE

A good unit for extension work or revision, pulling several strands on energy and electricity together.

Could be used in association with work on acid rain.

Suitable as it stands for more able fifth form students (there are a number of numerical problems).

ADAPTING THE UNIT

☐ The text is accessible to a wide range of students and the unit can be adapted for lower abilities by leaving out or substituting for the more difficult questions.

☐ The questions on page 5 are suitable for discussion in small groups. Each group may be allocated a selection of questions and asked to report back to the class.

☐ This work may also be linked to work on charging and discharging lead-acid accumulators.

FURTHER INFORMATION

If inexpensive lightweight batteries are developed, they will improve the payload against range balance but will do nothing to ease the speed of recharging.

Very large currents would be needed to recharge quickly and cables in the streets would not be able to cope with this.

NEW MATERIAL

☐ Two pages replacing page 5.
☐ Teachers' Notes for the new pages.

First published 1986

TEACHING NOTES

Answers to dicussion questions

Q1 *Electric vehicles are uncommon. Batteries are expensive, making electric vehicles costly. Half the payload is taken up by lead-acid batteries. Recharging is slow. The large mass of the batteries means vehicles are slow to accelerate. Electric vehicles tend to have a short range.*

Q2 *(a) Milk rounds involve lots of stops. This was no problem for a horse which would even learn the round!*

(b) Stopping and restarting wears out an engine.

It is an offence to leave a vehicle unattended with its engine running.

Q3 *(a) The heavy battery in a fork-lift truck provides an essential counterweight to the load when it is lifted.*

(b) No pollution by exhaust gases, quiet, rechargeable overnight.

Q4 *The C5s were classified as motor vehicles. They were too small and slow for their owners to feel safe on the roads.*

Q5 *Somebody has to bear the cost of spare batteries left at petrol stations. There comes a point when it is cheaper to have extra vehicles than to use several battery exchanges per day. There is no satisfactory way of finding out exactly how much energy the battery will give, unlike petrol where the volume sold can be measured.*

Q6 *Personal answers.*

Q7 *Hybrid vehicles would have the cost weight problems of two vehicles loaded onto one.*

Q8 *Coal or nuclear fuels are not normally used as sources of energy for transportation and are more plentiful than oil.*

(Electricity from nuclear fuel does not add to the greenhouse effect.)

Q9 *The overall efficiency in harnessing primary sources of energy for electric vehicles is*
$30\% \times 70\% = 21\%$

This is less than burning petrol directly in car engines (23%) (This efficiency may be exceeded by new petrol engines, making this comparison even worse for the electric vehicle.)

Q10 *(a) The electricity supply industry would not be able to cope with such a sudden change. It would take many years to build more power stations to meet the increased demand.*

(b) Electric vehicles are less efficient (see answer to Q9) at harnessing primary energy sources. If the extra electricity for them were generated by burning a fuel (such as coal or oil), the output of carbon dioxide would increase. Reduction of greenhouse gases and acid rain could only be achieved by using nuclear power stations or by harnessing non-fuel renewables like hydro, wind, tidal, etc.

(c) Probably not. The rapid changes would involve building new power stations, vehicles and factories. This would require large amounts of energy.

(d) Personal answers.

The problem of vehicle weight is interesting. The more batteries an electric vehicle has, the greater the distance it can travel. However, a vehicle with many batteries has less space to carry a load. Thus an electric vehicle's specification always involves a trade-off between payload and range. You could say that an electric vehicle uses half its energy supply just moving itself about empty! Perhaps the day of the electric vehicle will come when cheap, lightweight batteries are developed.

Figure 8 The Sinclair C5 electric tricycle used milk float technology in 1985

Questions for discussion

Q1   Draw up a list of the advantages and disadvantages of electric vehicles. Use the list to help you decide why electric vehicles are still uncommon.

Q2   Most of the electric vehicles in Britain are milk floats.
Find out or use your general knowledge to suggest answers to these questions.
(a)   Horse-drawn milk floats were used before electric ones. What were the advantages of using horses?
(b)   Why is an electric vehicle more suitable for a milk round than a petrol or diesel vehicle?

Q3   Fork-lift trucks are used in factories to carry goods around. They are nearly always electric.
(a)   Explain how the large weight of the batteries is an advantage when raising a load.
(b)   What are the advantages of having fork-lift trucks electrically-powered?

Q4   Sir Clive Sinclair invented the C5 electric tricycle. It was introduced with much hype in 1985. He saw it as a popular, cheap, non-polluting runabout, an answer to the problems of crowded roads.
What do you think were the advantages and disadvantages of the C5? Suggest why it never caught on.

Figure 9 A fork-lift truck

Q5 A problem with electric cars is their short range compared with that of petrol cars. Batteries are expensive – one third to one half of the cost a new car.

If electric cars became popular, it has been suggested that petrol stations could run battery exchange schemes. Instead of filling up with petrol, the electric motorist could have a flat battery exchanged for a fully-charged one.

How would such a scheme work in practice? What problems might there be?

Q6 What difference would it make to an average family if they had to change their petrol driven car for a electric one?

Q7 Some people believe that vehicles with both electric motors and petrol engines, would be more practical. These 'hybrid' vehicles would be able to run from their batteries or on petrol. A few experimental buses have been built but no 'hybrid' cars. What do you think would be the advantages and disadvantages of the hybrid car?

Q8 Look back at the section on recharging. An expert on electric vehicles has said, 'Electric vehicles are a way we can burn coal and nuclear fuel on our streets'. What did he mean?

Q9 Only about 30 per cent of the primary sources of energy put into power stations is converted into electricity. But electric motors are more efficient than petrol engines. Overall, does this mean that electric vehicles use primary sources of energy (oil, coal, nuclear etc.) more efficiently?

Q10 A new political party, 'The UltraGreens', proposes to prevent acid rain and the greenhouse effect by passing laws to:
● stop the manufacture of petrol and diesel vehicles within two years,
● switch production to electric vehicles,
● ban all petrol and diesel vehicles from the roads within seven years.

The party claims this would reduce pollution and create more employment in manufacturing.

(a) Do you think electricity supplies could cope with electric vehicles?

(b) Would the new laws be likely to effect the amount of acid gases and carbon dioxide released into the air?

(c) Do you think the proposals are realistic?

(d) Do you think the policy would be popular with voters?

Drinking Alcohol

Science content

Drug abuse, alcohol, body processes.

Science curriculum links
AT3   Processes of life

Syllabus links
- GCSE Science, Biology, Chemistry,
- Sixth-form General Studies
- Mathematics

Cross-curricular themes
- Health Education
- Citizenship

Lesson time
   1–1½ hours
   (homework possible)

Links with other SATIS materials
508   Risks
909   AIDS
1010 Can it be done?
      (questions 5, 6, 14, 31)

NERIS
Search on
      ALCOHOL
and   UPPER SECONDARY.

Additional search terms
      ALCOHOL ABUSE

STUDENT ACTIVITIES

☐ Experiment: How much alcohol is in a drink?

☐ Information and questions: What does alcohol do to your body?

☐ Information and questions (suitable for discussion in small groups): How much alcohol is safe?

USE

May be used as extension work on the nervous system. Suitable for all abilities. Practical work will require a variety of glasses.

The most popular use of this unit has been in sixth-form general studies and GCSE biology. Girls like the scientific approach to a social issue. It has also been used in PSE courses on drug abuse and in conjunction with Salter's 'Drinks' topic.

ADAPTING THE UNIT

☐ This unit is very suitable for most abilities as it stands. 'One of my most successful units because the kids can relate to it!'

☐ Some teachers demonstrate Part 1 to save time.

☐ An additional exercise is to to grade wines, spirits and beers by their percentage of alcohol using the labels on empties, and which teaching staff could easily provide. Low alcohol wines and beers should be included.

☐ Some teachers have expanded the unit to deal with the risk of death through drinking and related accidents.

☐ Has been linked to TACADE material.

FURTHER INFORMATION

Alcohol free means not more than 0.05 per cent (alcohol by volume).

'De-alcoholised' means not more than 0.5 per cent.

'Low alcohol' has no legal standing, but the Government intends to set a figure of not more than 1.2 per cent.

See *Which?*, Low-alcohol beers, December 1989, published by the Consumers' Association.

NEW MATERIAL

Since the unit was written, concerns about the effects of alcohol have increased. A new page 7 is provided.

First published 1986

As Figure 7 shows, an average man reaches the legal limit for drinking after about five units of alcohol. Each unit of alcohol takes about one hour to be broken down in the liver. Someone who has had two pints of beer will need about four hours to clear their blood of alcohol.

---

8 Low alcohol lagers and wines contain a wide range of alcohol content. How many pints of the following drinks would put someone at the legal limit for driving?

(a) 1% alcohol by volume lager

(b) 0.5% alcohol by volume 'de-alcoholised' lager

(c) 0.05% alcohol by volume 'alcohol-free' lager

How much alcohol is safe?

If you are doing anything that requires concentration, such as operating machinery or driving a vehicle, you should not drink at all. Even a small amount will affect your judgement.

Regular drinking can damage your health. Medical experts suggest that a man who drinks more than 21 units a week is risking his health. For a woman, this figure is 14 units.

Both of these values are for a person of average size. Experts recommend two periods of 48 hours without alcohol during the week for the body to recover.

Alcohol raises blood pressure and may cause a stroke. Alcohol contributes to obesity, beer belly for example, and is linked with some forms of cancer.

Alcohol not only damages health directly but may lead to behaviour which causes injury or death. Alcohol makes some people very unsociable. They tend to become aggressive and involve themselves in fights. Young motorists who drink are much more likely to have accidents than older drivers who drink the same amount. They are inexperienced drivers; they are inexperienced drinkers.

You should also remember that tiredness and other factors affect the way you react to drink. Having 5 units of alcohol before driving is not only dangerous but it may also put you well over the legal limit – especially if you are lightweight or female. Drinking early in the day can cause you to be over the limit. Three units is a more sensible limit to use, or better still, do not drink and drive.

In the USA some states have passed new laws to stop mothers abusing drugs during pregnancy. Many babies of alcoholic mothers suffer fetal alcohol syndrome – a shrivelled-up appearance, small head and low birth-weight. It can affect a child's health for the rest of its life. Alcoholic mothers have even been sent to prison during their pregnancy to prevent them drinking and putting their babies at risk.

Questions for group discussion

Q1   Karen, Jane, Paul and Scott got together for a few drinks one evening. This is what each drank:

- Karen: *three glasses of wine and a double vodka and tonic.*
- Jane: *one glass of sherry and three glasses of orange juice.*
- Paul: *five pints of beer.*
- Scott: *two pints of beer and a single whisky.*

(a)   Work out how many alcohol units each had.

(b)   Who is legally fit to drive home?

(c)   Who is most fit to drive home?

(d)   How long would Paul have to wait until he is legally fit to drive home? (Assume he is an average size man.)

Q2   Suppose that these people drink this much alcohol each night. Work out how many units per week each consumes. Suggest a sensible drinking programme for each of them in view of what they like to drink.

Q3   What happens to the motorist who goes out and has too much to drink? Here's an answer to the problem from a small town in the USA.

Drivers who have had too much to drink are advised to call the police for a free ride home.

What do you think are the advantages and disadvantages of this arrangement? Would it be practical in the UK?

Using Radioactivity

Science content

Ionising radiations, properties, beneficial uses.

Science curriculum links
AT8 Explaining how materials behave

Syllabus links
○ GCSE Science, Biology, Chemistry, Physics
○ Sixth-form General Studies

Cross-curricular themes
○ Health Education

Lesson time
1–1½ hours
(homework possible)

Links with other SATIS materials
109 Nuclear Power
807 Radiation – how much do you get?
808 Nuclear Fusion
1010 Can it be done? (question 7)

SATIS 16–19
74 Radionuclides for measuring flow

NERIS
Search on
MEDICAL RADIOLOGY
or
MEDICAL RADIOGRAPHY
Additional search terms
RADIOACTIVE ISOTOPES
RADIATION
and UPPER SECONDARY

STUDENT ACTIVITIES

☐ Part 1 Reading information. What is radioactivity?

☐ Part 2 Reading and answering questions. Radioactivity in use: measuring thickness of paper, smoke detector, checking welds in pipes, tracing movements of materials, gamma camera, sterilizing, treating cancer, safety.

☐ Part 3 Problem-solving. Suitable for discussion or written answers. Six examples for students to select an appropriate radioisotope from the data.

USE

The unit is suitable for most abilities. It is excellent for illustrating the applications of radioisotopes following work on radioactivity.

ADAPTING THE UNIT

The problem-solving in Part 3 works well as a small group activity with each group having a different problem and reporting to the class.

OTHER RESOURCES

☐ BBC TV 'Science Topics, Radioactivity'.

☐ The UKAEA's video *Isotopes in Action* links well. It is available for purchase at £10 for VHS and Betamax cassettes and runs for 25 minutes. Now available from Video Distribution, Room 1.28, Building 329, Harwell Laboratory, Oxfordshire OX11 0RA.

FURTHER INFORMATION

☐ Page 4 line 2, the isotope used should say indium-113 (and not iridium-113). It has a half-life of 99 minutes. Although the distinction is not made at school level, the isotope is metastable, indium-113m. Similarly, where the text refers to technetium-99 (99Tc) this is in fact technetium-99m (99mTc), a gamma emitter with a half-life of 6 hours. (The difference between these nuclides is significant- 99Tc is a $-\beta$ emitter with a half-life of 2.12×10^5 years.)

☐ Food irradiation. Since this unit was first published, the Government intend to permit the sale of certain foods which have been irradiated with gamma rays to preserve them. This has aroused controversy. *Which?* published by the Consumers' Association gives regular updates on this issue.

First published 1986

Looking at Motor Oil

Science content

Lubrication, alkanes,
molecular shape, viscosity and
temperature.

Science curriculum links
AT 1 Exploration of science
AT 8 Explaining how materials
        behave

Syllabus links
  ○ GCSE Science, Chemistry,
     Physics
  ○ Technology

Lesson time
     1–2½ hours

Links with other SATIS materials
504   How Safe is Your Car?

NERIS
Search on
        ENGINE OILS

STUDENT ACTIVITIES

☐ Reading and questions: lubrication for engines; viscosity
   decreases with temperature; functions of engine oil.

☐ Practical work: investigating the viscosity of oil.

USE

Use as an extension to hydrocarbon chemistry or to illustrate the
effect of temperature on a physical property (viscosity).

The experiment is messy. Students should take care not to get oil
on their skin or clothes.

ADAPTING THE UNIT

☐ Survey engine oils in shops and petrol stations.

☐ The practical work may be omitted.

☐ Many teachers demonstrate the experiment.

☐ The experiment may be better done outside. (If oil is spilled,
   there is a danger of slipping on the floor.)

☐ The experiment may provide an opportunity for assessment of
   skills for AT1.

☐ The following method may be used to compare the viscosity
   of motor oils at room temperature. Use a perspex tube about
   1.1 m long. Plug one end with a rubber bung. Put marks on
   the tube 1 metre apart. Time ball bearings as they fall through
   1 m. Repeat several times for each oil. The ball bearings may
   be removed after the experiment.

First published 1986

Test-tube Babies

STUDENT ACTIVITIES

☐ Reading information: cause of infertility; female and male reproductive systems; sperm count; ovulation; in vitro fertilization.

☐ Discussion in small groups: embryo research; surrogate motherhood; storing embryos frozen; manipulation of genes; cost of achieving a pregnancy; applications to animals.

USE

The unit may be used as extension to work on reproduction and is suitable for all abilities. The unit has been successfully used in the third year and with CPVE students.

It is recommended that this unit should be used by a teacher who knows the subject well and has a close relationship with the class. It is therefore not recommended for 'cover'.

ADAPTING THE UNIT

☐ The BBC audio tape, 'Test-tube Babies', enhances the material in the unit. It is designed to be heard after students have read the information as a prelude to discussion.

☐ Additional questions are provided to make the reading more active.

☐ Can be used with recent newspaper articles to aid discussion.

FURTHER INFORMATION

Since the Warnock Report, a Voluntary Licensing Authority, set up in 1985, has policed embryo research. It will become the Statutory Licensing Authority following the March 1990 vote in Parliament to permit experimentation on human embryos up to and including 14 days old. (Spain and Sweden are the only other European countries to have legalised this research too.)

The then Secretary of State for health, Kenneth Clarke, said that research on embryos would promote advances in the treatment of infertility and expand understanding of congenital diseases and miscarriages. It would lead to safer forms of contraception and help in the detection of faulty genes responsible for inherited abnormalities. Another legal case concerning frozen embryos, the first in the US, was heard during 1989. A divorced woman, Mary Sue Davis, sued her former husband, Junior Lewis Davis, for their seven embryos, being kept in liquid nitrogen at a

First published 1986

laboratory. Her ex-husband argued that he did not want to become a father against his will.

The judge decided that embryos are human, that they are not property and that human life begins at conception. It was in the interests of the child or children that they be available for implantation.

A group of researchers reported in 1990 that it was possible to remove one cell from an eight cell embryo to test for specific genetic diseases without damaging the embryo.

The British Medical Association has agreed to support surrogate motherhood in some cases. It is against British law for a surrogate mother to benefit financially.

OTHER RESOURCES

Human IVF, embryo research, fetal tissue for research and treatment, and abortion: International Information. Jennifer Gunning, February 1990. (Department of Health) HMSO. £7.50. ISBN 0 11 321280 1.

Questions on the text

Q1 *What do the following words used in the unit mean? (a) infertile, (b) conceive, (c) sperm count, (d) ovulation, (e) fertility drugs, (f) in vitro fertilization, (g) ova.*

Q2 *How long should a couple try for a baby before seeking medical help?*

Q3 *When during a woman's menstrual cycle is she most likely to conceive?*

Q4 *Why might the male partner be advised to wear baggy underpants?*

Q5 *What can be done to help men who have a low sperm count?*

Q6 *How can a woman find out when she is ovulating?*

Q7 *In what circumstances may in vitro fertilization be used to help a couple conceive?*

The Story of Fritz Haber

Science content

Ammonia, fertilizers, explosives, chlorine.

Science curriculum links
AT7   Making new materials
AT17 The nature of science

Syllabus links
○ GCSE Science, Chemistry
○ Sixth-form General Studies
○ History

Cross-curricular themes
○ Citizenship

Lesson time
1–2 hours
(homework possible)

Links with other SATIS materials
408   Industrial Gases
505   Making Fertilizers
810   High Pressure Chemistry

BBC Radio SATIS Topics 14–16
The Story of Fritz Haber.

NERIS
Search on
HABER PROCESS

STUDENT ACTIVITIES

☐ Reading: the life of Fritz Haber, best remembered for the synthesis of ammonia, although much of his work was on chemical warfare. Haber was highly patriotic and his work involved many ethical and moral issues.

☐ Questions: for written answers or group discussion.

USE

May be used to extend work on chlorine or on the synthesis of ammonia. Suitable for average ability students, although passive reading is required. The unit reflects the aims of AT 7 and AT 17 showing the development and historical importance of the conversion of raw materials into useful products.

ADAPTING THE UNIT

☐ The text may be made more accessible with simple activities, such as:
List the chemical elements and compounds mentioned in the text.
Fritz Haber died in 1934. Make a list of the dates of the main events in his life.

☐ The BBC Radio programme of the same title supports the text in this unit and is designed to be heard after reading the text, as a prelude to discussion.

☐ Dramatisations of the story, role-plays and formal debates on the issues have been developed from this unit. (In one case, the play reached the finals of a national drama competition!)

☐ SATIS unit 810, *High Pressure Chemistry*, follows on from this unit, describing the work of Carl Bosch.

First published 1986

The Price of Food

Science content

Food production, food chains, food processing.

Science curriculum links
AT1   Exploration of science
AT2   The variety of life
AT3   Processes of life

Syllabus links
o   GCSE Science, Biology
o   Sixth-form General Studies
o   Technology (Home Economics)
o   Geography

Cross-curricular themes
o   Health Education
o   Economic Awareness

Lesson time
   1 hour
   Homework (survey)

Links with other SATIS materials
102   Food from Fungus
104   What's in our Food?
108   Fibre in Your Diet
703   Vegetarianism
901   The Chinese Cancer Detectives

SATIS 16–19
   Food Irradiation

NERIS
Search on
   FOOD PRODUCTION
   and ECONOMICS
   and UPPER SECONDARY

STUDENT ACTIVITIES

☐ Part 1   Survey (data gathering): food prices (to be done at home).

☐ Part 2   Discussion in small groups: what decides the price of food?

USE

The unit may be used for all abilities as extension or introduction to work on diet and health. Less able students may need help with completing the table.

ADAPTING THE UNIT

☐ Name three foods you think are good value and three which are poor value.

☐ Produce a leaflet advising shoppers about what decides the price of food.

FURTHER INFORMATION

The Government intends to permit the sale of irradiated food and this type of processing may be considered in the discussion. *Which?*, the magazine of the Consumers' Association is a good source of up-to-date information on this topic.

First published 1986

Spectacles and Contact Lenses

Science content

Common defects of the eye and their correction.

Science curriculum links
AT1   Exploration of science
AT15 Using light and
         electromagnetic radiation

Syllabus links
○   GCSE Science, Biology,
      Physics

Cross-curricular themes
○   Health Education

Lesson time
      1–2 hours
      (homework possible)

Links with other SATIS materials
306   Fibre Optics
406   Blindness
1010   Can it be done?
          (question 19)

STUDENT ACTIVITIES

☐ Reading and questions: short sight, long sight, accommodation, astigmatism, history of spectacles, spectacle lenses, contact lenses.

☐ Practical observation and questions: looking at different spectacle lenses and considering their uses.

☐ Survey of sight defects (data collection): looking for patterns in different age groups.

☐ Questions for discussion: driving and eyesight (new material).

USE

As extension to work on the structure and function of the eye.

Much of the unit is accessible to all abilities.

ADAPTING THE UNIT

☐ Parts of the unit may be used separately.

☐ The survey on page 5 has been very popular. It makes a good starting point for less able students.

☐ Class summaries of results have been produced as a wall chart and provide a satisfying end point to the work.

☐ Less able students have been helped by making a glossary of difficult words.

☐ The sight survey provides opportunities for assessment of skills for AT 1 – stating patterns derived from data etc.

☐ The new material may be used at the end of Part 1 or Part 2.

FURTHER INFORMATION

Page 2 The eye test is no longer free on the NHS, except for people in exempt categories. The cost varies between £11 and £15. Students should be aware of the importance of regular eye tests, which not only provide a check on sight but detect early signs of other diseases like diabetes and glaucoma.

Part 2 Students may need help in identifying types of spectacle lenses. School laboratory lenses are based on simple shapes and are converging (convex in shape) or diverging (concave in shape). It is more difficult to tell whether meniscus lenses, which are used for spectacles and contact lenses, are converging or diverging.

Page 4, section B A converging (convex) lens for long sight held at arm's length makes things look smaller and upside-down. When

First published 1986

held close to something like writing, a converging lens magnifies.

Diverging lenses (concave) for short sight, always make things look smaller and upright.

In future many eye defects may be corrected by operating on the eye. Two thirds of the eye's focusing is done by the cornea. An operation called radial keratotomy, surgically flattening the cornea by making a series of cuts to correct short sight, has been performed on about 300 000 people, mostly in the USSR. Four out of every five patients have had normal sight restored.

A new technique, photorefractive keratectomy may prove to be more reliable and has been tested in Britain. It uses an eximer laser beam producing ultraviolet light. The laser vaporises molecules on the surface of the eye enabling the surgeon to skim away a small amount of the cornea about 3 to 4 millimetres wide and up to 40-thousandths of a millimetre deep. The amount removed is calculated and controlled by computer. If all goes well, the operation may become more widely available.

NEW MATERIAL

Questions for discussion on driving and eyesight.

The driving test requires the motorist to read (with glasses or contact lenses if worn) a car number plate with figures on it 79.4 mm high from a distance of 20.5 m.

A motorist needs good eyesight!

Someone applying for a driving licence in Britain has to declare that he or she has good eyesight. A simple eyesight test is part of the driving test.

> **Q1**   *What eye test must you take to get a UK driving licence?*
> *(If you need to find out, look at an application form in a main post office.)*

Maybe you would like to see if you can meet the eyesight requirements.

> **Q2**   *Would somebody with sight in only one eye be able to pass the test? Explain the disadvantage of being able to see with one eye.*
>
> **Q3**   *How long does a British driving licence last?*
>
> **Q4**   *What happens if the driver's eyesight deteriorates?*

Motorists in many other countries have to take a more thorough eyesight test to get a driving licence. And their eyesight must be retested every few years, especially after the age of fifty.

In the US, people taking the driving test have their eyesight tested by a machine for:
acuity, depth and colour perception, imbalance, double vision and field of vision.

> **Q5**   *Which aspect from the US list does the British driving test assess?*

For a British driving licence you must say if there is anything wrong with your eyesight, such as double vision, tunnel vision, partial loss of sight or night blindness.

> **Q6**   *(a)   What is common to both the British list and the US list?*
> *(b)   Where do the lists differ?*
> *(c)   Say how each of these aspects of vision are important for driving.*
>
> **Q7**   *It is a criminal offence to drive a motor vehicle without being able to meet the eyesight standard. Would you recommend any changes in the eyesight test for British motorists? Explain your answer.*

The Pesticide Problem

Science content
Pests, pesticides, environmental safety, horticulture, agriculture.

Science curriculum links
AT1 Exploration of science
AT2 The variety of life

Syllabus links
○ GCSE Science, Biology, Chemistry

Cross-curricular themes
○ Environment
○ Economic Awareness

Lesson time
1 hour

Links with other SATIS materials
110 Hilltop – an agricultural problem
402 DDT and Malaria
906 IT in Greenhouses

NERIS
Search on
PESTICIDES and UPPER SECONDARY
Addition search term
PEST CONTROL

STUDENT ACTIVITIES

Suitable for students working in groups or for individual study.

☐ Reading the introduction: pests, pesticides and growing food. (New material provides questions related to the text.)

☐ Decision-making: an exercise in classifying three slug killers.

☐ Evaluation of evidence and data analysis: trials of slug killers.

USE

May be used as an extension to lessons on environmental issues and the management of artificial ecosystems.

ADAPTING THE UNIT

☐ Design an advertisement for a slug killer to go in a newspaper or gardening magazine.

☐ Students who are less familiar with the problems of pests in gardening and agriculture may benefit from an introductory discussion.

NEW MATERIAL

Questions to draw out points made in the introduction to the unit.

First published 1986

These questions are about page 1.

> **Q1** Name three animals that are pests.
>
> **Q2** Why do you think of these animals as pests?
>
> **Q3** What do farmers and gardeners do to reduce the problem of pests?
>
> **Q4** What do the terms 'pesticide' and 'insecticide' mean?
>
> **Q5** DDT was used as an insecticide. It has now been banned. Why?
>
> **Q6** What properties should a good pesticide have?

These questions are about page 2.

> **Q7** Why do pesticides have to be tested for safety?
>
> **Q8** What conditions must be met before they can be sold?
>
> **Q9** Suggest why pesticides should be properly labelled when sold.
>
> **Q10** You grow lettuces commercially to sell to supermarkets. Your best friend is a chemist who has invented a new pesticide. It should be a real money-spinner! But its formula must be kept from competing companies as long as possible. Your friend pleads with you to try it out secretly first. What do you say?

Air Pollution – where does it come from?

Science content

Sources of pollution, pollutant gases.

Science curriculum links

AT5   Human influences on the Earth

Syllabus links
- GCSE Science, Biology, Chemistry
- Geography
- Sixth-form General Studies

Cross-curricular themes
- Environment

Lesson time
  1 hour

Links with other SATIS materials

801   The Water Pollution Mystery
902   Acid Rain
1209 The Greenhouse Effect
1103 Save the Salmon

SATIS 16–19

12   Trouble with CFCs
69   Living in a greenhouse

NERIS

Search on
  POLLUTANT GASES

Additional search term
  AIR POLLUTION

STUDENT ACTIVITIES

☐ Data analysis and evaluation exercise: drawing a bar chart, on pollutant gases CO, SO_2, NO, NO_2, NH_3, H_2S and hydrocarbons.

☐ Data interpretation and class discussion: sulphur dioxide.

USE

May be used as extension work on gases of the air. A good homework exercise. Many discussion points may emerge from the graphs.

ADAPTING THE UNIT

☐ There is an error in the graph paper printed on page 3. The graph paper has large divisions sub-divided into six. A replacement page is provided.

☐ It has been used in conjunction with the Clean Air Act data.

☐ Extend the graph in Figure 3 with the new data provided.

FURTHER INFORMATION

There is increased interest in other pollutants, not mentioned in the tables – in particular carbon dioxide and methane which are implicated in global warming and in CFCs which are implicated in both ozone layer damage and global warming.

UPDATING INFORMATION

Table 2 You may wish to change the following:

carbon monoxide   **2000**
sulphur dioxide   volcanoes and **biological processes 100 – 200**
nitrogen oxides   **75**

Figure 2 A replacement is provided.

Figure 3 Changes in the production of SO_2 by human activities since 1850

year	mass of SO_2 in millions of tonnes per year
1980	4.8
1982	4.2
1984	3.6
1986	3.9
1987	3.9

The graph is printed on a millimetre scale. Using a ruler calibrated with millimetres, the graph may be extended with the data.

First published 1986

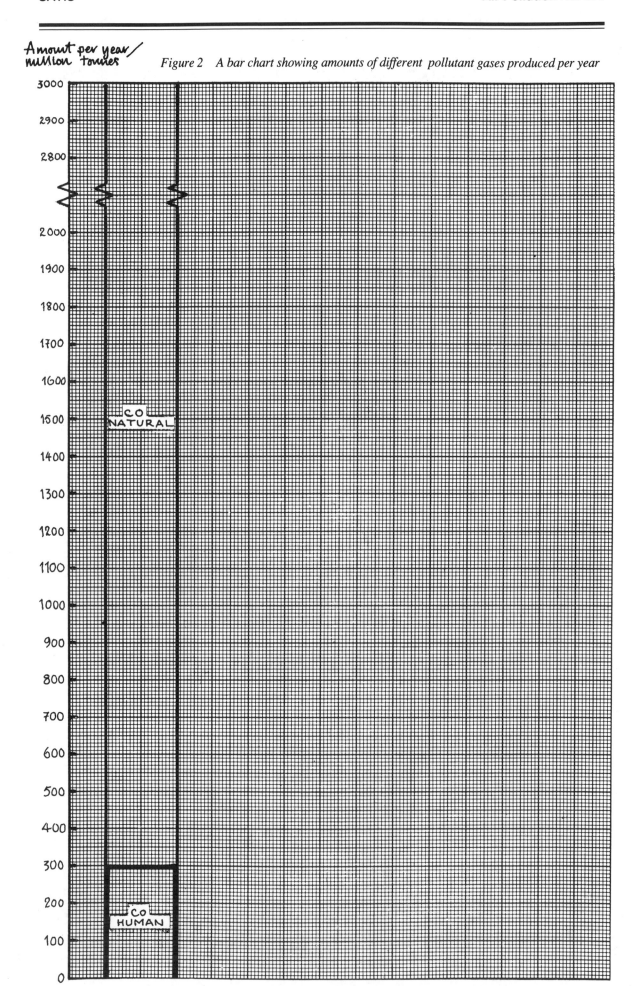

Amount per year/
million tonnes

Figure 2   A bar chart showing amounts of different pollutant gases produced per year

Living with Kidney Failure

Science content

Kidney function, kidney machine (an example of life-supporting technology), kidney transplants.

Science curriculum links
AT 3 Processes of life

Syllabus links
- GCSE Science, Biology
- Sixth-form General Studies

Cross-curricular themes
- Health Education
- Citizenship
- Economic Awareness

Lesson time
1 hour with prior homework

Links with other SATIS materials
503 Paying for National Health
603 The Heart Pacemaker
707 Artificial Limbs
1010 Can it be done? (questions 8, 9, 19, 39)

BBC Radio SATIS topics 14–16
Living with Kidney Failure

SATIS 16–19
7 Kidney transplants

NERIS
Search on KIDNEYS

STUDENT ACTIVITIES

- ☐ Reading and test: information on kidneys and kidney failure. This part may be set as homework before a discussion lesson.
- ☐ Structured discussion: briefing sheets for groups of four students.
- ☐ Class discussion of general points.

USE

May be used following work on digestion or excretion. The material is better suited to upper or middle ability students. It is essential that students prepare thoroughly for their roles.

ADAPTING THE UNIT

- ☐ The general briefing on kidney function, kidney failure and the short test may be used separately and possibly along with the BBC Radio programme, 'Living with Kidney Failure'.
- ☐ The BBC Radio programme, 'Living with Kidney Failure' may be used to follow the reading of the general briefing. It describes the experience of an 18 year-old hairdresser who was faced with the choices of dialysis, a kidney transplant or dying.
- ☐ The material can be used for individual work, students reading all the information and answering the questions on the chairperson's briefing sheet.
- ☐ Instead of group discussion, students could give short talks, followed by a full class discussion.

NEW MATERIAL AND UPDATING INFORMATION

Three new pages are provided for EB2.1, EB2.2 and EB3.

The following minor alterations may be made to the original pages. The situation for dialysis and transplants has altered slightly. Dialysis using a bag of fluid while patients go about their normal activities (called continuous ambulatory peritoneal dialysis), mentioned on teachers' notes ii, is also outlined in the BBC programme. Students may know somebody receiving this type of treatment.

- ☐ On GB2
  'Kidney machines – artificial kidneys which the patient must use two or three times a week (more details in Expert's Briefing 1) *or a fluid exchange system in a portable bag which does the same job.*'
  'But over 2000 people who could be treated die ...'
- ☐ In EB1.2, the dialysis time of 10 hours mentioned is a maximum, the time now being **between 5 and 10 hours**.

First published 1986

Living with Kidney Failure: Expert's Briefing 2

What are kidney transplants?

You will shortly be taking part in a group discussion on kidney treatment. You are the only one in your group to read this sheet, so you will be the expert on kidney transplants. The Chairperson in your group will ask the kind of questions a 'man or woman in the street' might ask. Try to answer them as simply as possible, in your own words.

Sometimes, doctors can replace a failed kidney with a healthy one, taken from a human donor. This is a **kidney transplant**.

The kidney may come from a live donor or from a person who has just died.

Live donors We have two kidneys, so one can be donated. This is most commonly done by relatives. The chances of a kidney being rejected by the patient's body are less if the kidney comes from a close relative. However, only about 10 per cent of transplant kidneys come from live donors.

People who have died To be of any use, the kidneys need to be working when they are taken from the donor's body. This means that the only kidneys suitable are from a person who died in an intensive care unit of a hospital, while being treated on an artificial ventilator. Although dead, the person's body is kept going by machine while doctors carry out tests to check the brain is really dead. Kidneys from these 'brain dead' donors can be removed, cooled down and used within 48 hours.

> **How can more kidneys be made available?**
>
> Some people have suggested an opting-out system. You would have to carry a card, or register on a computer if you did *not* want your kidneys used. This would have the disadvantage of removing the 'gift' of organ donation which gives bereaved relatives comfort.
>
> A better suggestion is the 'required request' which makes sure that doctors never turn a ventilator off without first finding out relatives' wishes.

Figure 1 A Donor Card

Kidney Donor Card

Your kidneys could help someone to live after your death

Keep the card with you at all times in a place where it will be found quickly

YOUR KIDNEYS COULD SAVE LIVES

Although hundreds of successful kidney transplants are carried out each year, many more kidneys are needed. A successful kidney transplant means a new lease of life for somebody who has fallen ill because their kidneys have stopped working. People with kidney transplants can live a full and active life. They can work. They can go on holiday. they can enjoy life and living far more than when survival depends on the regular use of a kidney machine.

I have decided to help–what can I do?

Make your wishes known to your next-of-kin and carry this card when it has been signed by both of you.

Are all kidneys suitable?

Kidneys for transplantation should be removed from the body within half an hour of death. Delay means that they suffer serious damage. Therefore kidneys are only taken

I (full name) ....
Request that my kidneys be used after my death for transplantation or, if found unsuitable, for research.

Signature of donor .... Date ....

The above-named person has discussed his/her wish with me and I do not object to that wish being complied with.

(Name of next-of-kin) ....

of (address) ....

....

.... Tel ....

Signature of next-of-kin .... Date ....

from people who die in hospital usually following admission in an emergency.

Success also depends on good "tissue matching". Donated kidneys are compared with the tissue characteristics of all those in the country waiting for a transplant and offered to the best matching recipients. The more donors there are, the wider the choice, the better the chance of a good tissue match – and a successful transplant.

Did you know that your eyes could also be used after death to restore somebody else's sight? Information can be obtained from the Royal National Institute for the Blind, 224, Great Portland Street, London W.1.

Prepared by the Health Departments & Central Office of Information 1974
576881/6000M/2.78/LOM   KD1A

The best kidneys come from young, healthy donors. Often, these are people who have been killed in road accidents.

Kidneys are not taken from a person's body without permission from close relatives. Some people carry a signed Donor Card (Figure 1). This shows that they wished their kidneys and other organs to be used in transplants. The relatives' wishes will still be taken into account even if a Donor Card is found. If relatives object, the kidneys are not removed.

Problems with kidney transplants

Shortage of donors There are not enough donated kidneys available to allow every suitable patient to have a transplant. This is because there is a shortage of donors. In many cases families are not asked if they would like to donate organs from a relative who has died.

Rejection Unless the new kidney comes from an identical twin, it will not match the patient's own body perfectly. Doctors try to match the new kidney as closely as possible. Even so, the body is bound to reject the kidney to some extent. Transplant patients are given medicines to control rejection, but these medicines may have unpleasant side-effects.

If there is serious rejection of the kidney, the patient may need another transplant.

Living with Kidney Failure: Expert's Briefing 3

Statistics about kidney treatment

You will shortly be taking part in a group discussion on kidney treatment. You are the only one in your group to read this sheet, so you will be the expert on statistics about kidney treatment. The Chairperson in your group will ask the kind of questions a 'man or woman in the street' might ask. Try to answer them as simply as possible in your own words. Your briefing is quite short but you have a calculation to do before the discussion starts.

Proportions of patients on different kinds of treatment

Around 1800 kidney failure patients a year are treated by transplants. The current waiting list is 3800. These patients make up some of the 7000 people with kidney failure who are treated by kidney machines or by a fluid exchange system using a bag which allows them to go about their normal activities. *About half the kidney machine patients have treatment at home. As many as 2000 patients a year may die through not receiving any treatment at all.

Cost of treatment

Treatment for kidney failure is very expensive. The figures given here are approximate.

1 The cost of a *transplant* is around £9,000 for the operation. Follow-up treatment costs around £3,500 per year.

2 For kidney machine treatment in hospital, the cost is around £16,000 per patient per year.

3 For kidney machine treatment at home, the cost is around £14,000 per patient per year.

4 For the fluid exchange system (CAPD) the cost is around £12,000 per patient per year.

Calculation

Work out the cost of keeping a kidney patient alive for three years by each of the treatment methods given above. You should assume the transplant works first time, though this is not always true.

The NHS treats most suitable patients except the very young and the very old.

*Called continuous ambulatory peritoneal dialysis, CAPD.

General points for discussion

Q1 *How would your life be affected if you had kidney failure and had to go on a machine two or three times a week?*

Q2 *At present, there are not enough kidney machines in Britain to treat everyone who is suffering from kidney failure. Why is this?*

Q3 *To provide enough kidney machines would cost the National Health Service money. Where should this money come from? The possibilities are:*
*   *spending more money on kidney machines and less on other parts of the Health Service,*
*   *spending more on the whole Health Service. This would mean increasing taxes, or cutting other services like education,*
*   *increasing transplantation so freeing more machines.*

Q4 *If you think the best answer is to spend less on other parts of the National Health Service, which parts do you think should be cut? Explain why.*

Q5 *Doctors sometimes have to turn away people who need kidney treatment because there are not enough kidney machines.*

This may mean these people will die. How should a doctor decide who to treat and who to turn away? Factors which doctors have to consider include:
*   *whether the patient is suitable for treatment,*
*   *whether treatment will help the patient,*
*   *whether the patient has dependants, such as a family,*
*   *the age of the patient.*

Q6 *How can we overcome the shortage of transplant kidneys?*

Q7 *Which members of your discussion group would be prepared to carry a Donor Card?*

Q8 *Which members of your group would be happy to leave parts of their body for medical experiments as well as transplants?*

Q9 *At present people's bodies are not used for transplants unless permission has already been given by the close relatives, even if they find a Donor Card. Should the system be changed so that everyone's kidneys were removed, unless relatives or a Donor Card said no?*

Q10 *Should the law be changed to make doctors find out the relatives' wishes?*

Physics and Cooking

Science content

Conduction, convection, radiation, surface area, expansion of gases, microwave cooking, insulation.

Science curriculum links
AT 13 Energy
AT 15 Using light and electromagnetic radiation

Syllabus links
○ GCSE Science
○ Physics
○ Technology (Cookery)

Lesson time
1–2 hours
(homework possible)

Links with other SATIS materials
SATIS units on food 102, 104, 108, 208, 703
SATIS units relating to insulation and energy transfer 106, 1006

STUDENT ACTIVITIES

Reading and answering questions. The cooking experiments are optional.

☐ Part 1   Information about heat transfer, the influence of surface area

☐ Part 2   Boiling eggs

☐ Part 3   Sponge cakes, microwave ovens

☐ Part 4   Baked Alaska

USE

As part of work on heat. Suitable for all abilities. May be used for homework. It is not necessary to make up the recipes.

ADAPTING THE UNIT

☐ Part 4 alone (15 minutes without recipe) deals with the concept of insulation.

☐ Parts 1 and 2 (30 minutes without recipe) deal with heat transfer.

☐ Successful as a 'fun' homework for students.

FURTHER INFORMATION

Since the unit was written, some cases of salmonella infection have been attributed to raw or partly cooked eggs. If concerns about the risk of salmonella infection remain, teachers should note the possibility of food poisoning from eating soft-boiled eggs and soft meringue and alert their students to this problem.

OTHER RESOURCES

☐ *Physics Plus*, volume two, Hobsons (1988), ISBN 1 85324 031 1, 'Cooking Pots' considers heat transfer through saucepans.

First published 1986

A Medicine to Control Bilharzia – Part 1

Science content

Infective organism, parasite, life cycle, sanitation, pollution, water management, immunization, medicine.

Science curriculum links
AT 2 The variety of life
AT 3 Processes of life
AT 5 Human influences on the Earth

Syllabus links
○ GCSE Science, Biology
○ Geography

Cross-curricular themes
○ Health Education

Lesson time
1–2 hours
(homework possible)

Links with other SATIS materials
210   The Pesticide Problem
305   Bilharzia – Part 2
402   DDT and Malaria

BBC Radio SATIS topics 14–16,
A Medicine to Control Bilharzia

STUDENT ACTIVITIES

☐ Reading information: bilharzia (snail fever) and the developing world, parasitic disease.

☐ Problem solving: suggesting solutions to infection by bilharzia.

☐ Discussing or answering questions.

USE

May be used as an extension to work on diseases and life cycles and to develop awareness of the importance of good sanitation and water management. Pages 1–4 could be set for homework to be followed by discussion of the problems and issues raised on page 5.

ADAPTING THE UNIT

☐ The BBC Radio programme supports material in the unit and describes work in Egypt to control bilharzia. It may be used before discussing answers to the questions on page 5.

☐ Debates and role-plays may be developed from some of the later questions.

☐ This unit may be used separately or together with Part 2, SATIS 305.

FURTHER INFORMATION

In a report on tropical diseases published by the World Health Organisation in 1990, bilharzia was said to affect two hundred million people in 76 countries worldwide.

Tropical diseases	Countries affected	Number of people infected in millions
Malaria	103	270
Bilharzia	76	200
Lymphatic filariasis	76	90
River blindness	34	17
Chagas disease	21	17
Leishmaniasis	80	12
Leprosy	121	11
African sleeping sickness	36	0.025

First published 1986

A Medicine to Control Bilharzia – Part 2

Science content

Medicine, structure of organic molecules, biochemical processes.

Science curriculum links
AT7 Making new materials
AT8 Explaining how materials behave
AT17 The nature of science

Syllabus links
- GCSE Science, Biology, Chemistry
- Technology

Cross-curricular themes
- Health Education

Lesson time
1–2 hours

Links with other SATIS materials
304 Bilharzia – Part 1
210 The Pesticide Problem
309 Microbes make Human Insulin
509 Homoeopathy
609 Hitting the Target
710 What is Biotechnology?
810 The Search for the Magic Bullet

BBC Radio SATIS topics 14–16
A Medicine to Control Bilharzia.

STUDENT ACTIVITIES

☐ Reading information: the stages in developing a new medicine.

☐ Questions: consideration of the molecular structure of medicines for bilharzia, reasons for safety testing, manufacturing large quantities of the medicine.

☐ Questions to answer or discuss.

USE

This unit describes the development and testing of a medicine. It is a demanding unit but worthwhile for upper ability students, illustrating the work of a major British industry.

ADAPTING THE UNIT

☐ This unit may be used separately or together with Part 1, SATIS 304.

☐ If students have not used Part 1, the BBC radio programme could provide an introduction to the problem of bilharzia.

☐ Omitting page 3 makes the unit considerably easier without losing the theme.

FURTHER INFORMATION

In a report on tropical diseases published by the World Health Organisation in 1990, bilharzia was said to affect two hundred million people in 76 countries worldwide.

One of the problems in developing medicines for a tropical disease like bilharzia, is the expense – $100 million or so.

Pharmaceutical companies are reluctant to bring a drug to the market if they are unlikely to realise a profit. Tropical countries can afford to spend little on health care and even less on research.

First published 1986

Fibre Optics and Telecommunications

Science content

Information transmission systems, electrical signals, optical fibre, laser light, total internal reflection.

Science curriculum links
AT12 IT including microelectronics
AT15 Using light and electromagnetic radiation
AT17 The nature of science

Syllabus links
○ GCSE Science, Physics
○ Technology

Lesson time
1 hour
(homework possible)

Links with other SATIS materials
507 Computers and jobs
905 The impact of IT
1108 Telephones

NERIS
Search on
FIBRE OPTICS
or on
OPTICAL FIBRES

STUDENT ACTIVITIES

☐ Reading and questions: advances in telephone communications, optical fibre technology.

☐ Questions to answer and discuss: the implications of advances in technology.

USE

May be used as part of work on communication systems or to extend work on reflection and refraction of light.

ADAPTING THE UNIT

☐ Page 5 may be omitted.

☐ Page 5 Students may work in small groups and report back to the class.

OTHER RESOURCES

Teletom (released in 1990) is a software item from British Telecom which allows students to simulate sending a telephone signal from the UK to the USA. The amplitude of the signal is shown graphically at various stages along the route.

NEW MATERIAL AND UPDATING INFORMATION

In 1990, 70 per cent of the trunk telephone network in Britain was optical.

Newer data is available for question 10 on page 5. (However, it has not been possible to get data for exactly the same countries.) A question on mobile phones has been added.

First published 1986

10   *This table shows the numbers of telephones per hundred people in different countries in 1988.*

Country	Number of telephones per hundred people
USA	93
Japan	81
West Germany	91
France	98
UK	86
Italy	77
Canada	103
Australia	103
Sweden	119
Brazil	16

(a) *Comment on these figures.*

(b) *In what ways can a good telephone system help the development of a country?*

It is estimated that 30 million portable phones will be in use in Europe by the year 2000. Four systems will be available.

- *Cellular – the system used by almost 3 million Europeans in 1990.*
- *Telepoint. A cheaper system which allows calls to be made but not to be received.*
- *PCN – an advanced version of the cellular system with smaller handsets.*
- *Satellite – the most expensive. A network of satellites will allow users to call from and be reached anywhere in the world.*

The table gives figures for the number of subscribers to mobile telephones in June 1990.

Country	Number of subscribers	Number of mobile phones per 1000 population
West Germany	199 000	3
France	224 000	4
UK	1032 000	18
Italy	104 000	2
Sweden	408 000	48

11   (a) *Which country has the most subscribers?*

(b) *Which country has the most mobile phones per head?*

(c) *Compare the figures for mobile phones with those for ordinary telephones in question 10.*

(d) *Motorola, a company in the USA, plans to have 77 satellites in service by 1999. Handsets for the satellite mobile phone service will cost about $3,500 (that is, about £2,000). How can the costs of such an expensive service be justified by the users?*

Chemicals from Salt

Science content

Chlor-alkali industry, manufacturing implications.

Science curriculum links
AT7 Making new materials

Syllabus links
○ GCSE Science, Chemistry

Cross-curricular themes
○ Environment
○ Economic Awareness

Lesson time
  1–2 hours
  (prior homework
  possible)

Links with other SATIS materials
408 Industrial Gases
904 Which Bleach?
1002 Quintonal – an Industrial
  Hazard

BBC Radio SATIS Topics 14–16
Chemicals from Salt

NERIS
Search on
  SALT and ELECTROLYSIS

STUDENT ACTIVITIES

☐ Reading information: electrolysis, flowing mercury cell (now being replaced by the membrane cell), making, using, costing and transporting the products.

☐ Problem-solving role-play: for groups of four students.

USE

May be used as extension work on electrolysis, properties of chlorine, hydrogen etc.

ADAPTING THE UNIT

☐ Using the comprehension questions in the new material for lower ability students.

☐ Using the BBC Radio programme. It is best heard after reading the introduction. The programme describes the flowing mercury cell, the Minamata incident in Japan, the safety precautions now taken and why there is a change to membrane cells.

FURTHER INFORMATION

Flowing mercury cells are being phased out for environmental reasons. ICI has available a poster on 'Chemicals from Salt' giving details of the membrane cell and the historical development of the chlor-alkali process.

There are changes in the use of some chemicals. The following alterations are suggested to Figure 4 on page 3.

☐ Delete 'swimming pools', 'aerosols' and 'fire-extinguishers' from the uses under 'CHLORINE'. (The use of CFCs is being phased out because of depletion of the ozone layer and hence this use of chlorine.)

☐ Add 'Swimming pools' to the uses under 'BLEACH'. (Bleach is now being used for water treatment rather than chlorine gas.)

It is suggested that the deletions could be made to the original master with correcting fluid or crossed out on the copies.

NEW MATERIAL

A diagram and summary of a membrane cell. Questions on the text to assist lower ability students.

First published 1986

The membrane cell

The modern process for electrolysis of salt solution uses a membrane cell. This cell contains no mercury. The membrane cell gives a very pure solution of sodium hydroxide and is replacing the older mercury cell technology.

Figure 3   A new membrane cell which is replacing the older mercury cells

Q1   What does electrolysis mean?

Q2   Name the three products of the electrolysis of salt solution.

Q3   In Figure 2, what is the total value of the products obtained from 1000 kg of salt?

Q4   What is the added value of 1000 kg of salt after electrolysis? (Don't forget the cost of electricity!)

Q5   The added value isn't all profit! What must it pay for?

Q6   Suppose you are running a new electrolysis plant. You have found someone who wants to buy the sodium hydroxide you produce, but no customers for the chlorine and hydrogen.
  (a) Could you make a profit?
  (b) What would you do with the other products?
  (c) Would it be better to keep the sodium hydroxide yourself to make bleach? You may have to waste the hydrogen if you could not find a buyer for it.

Q7   Figure 4 gives the chemicals that are made from salt and some of the things these chemicals are used to make. Which ones do you use personally?

The Second Law of – What?

Science content

Diffusion in nature, dissipation of useful energy, fuels, alternative sources of energy, photosynthesis.

Science curriculum links
AT5   Human influences on the Earth
AT13 Energy

Syllabus links
 ○ GCSE Science, Biology, Chemistry, Physics
 ○ Sixth-form General Studies
 ○ Technology

Cross-curricular themes
 ○ Environment

Lesson time
    1 hour
    (may be homework)

Links with other SATIS materials
107   Ashton Island
201   Energy from Biomass
301   Air Pollution
403   Britain's Energy Sources

Other energy units
109, 508, 601, 808, 902, 908, 1010.

SATIS 16–19
20   Energising an Indian village
21   Energy from the wind
46   Energy from the waves
63   Biogas

NERIS
Search on
      THERMODYNAMICS

STUDENT ACTIVITIES

Reading and answering questions: energy tends to spread out, why fuels are useful, alternative energy sources including biomass fuels.

USE

An excellent unit to draw together ideas on energy. The unit describes in simple terms the ideas behind the Second Law of Thermodynamics. A useful unit for homework or for independent study.

ADAPTING THE UNIT

☐ The unit is normally done unaltered.

First published 1986

Microbes make Human Insulin

Science content

Hormone, diabetes, insulin, gene, genetic engineering, ethical considerations.

Science curriculum links
AT3   Processes of life
AT4   Genetics and evolution
AT17 The nature of science

Syllabus links
○ GCSE Science, Biology
○ Sixth-form General Studies

Cross-curricular themes
○ Health Education

Lesson time
   1–2 hours
   (with prior homework)

Links with other SATIS materials
302   Living with Kidney Failure
609   Hitting the Target – with monoclonal antibodies
805   The Search for the Magic Bullet
1204 From Babylon to Biotechnology

BBC Radio SATIS Topics 14–16
   Microbes make Human Insulin

NERIS
Search on
    INSULIN
  or DIABETES
  or GENETIC ENGINEERING

STUDENT ACTIVITIES

☐ Reading and answering questions: the hormone insulin, the nature of diabetes.

☐ Reading and questions: the development of genetically engineered insulin.

☐ Discussion points for students working in groups of three or four: the uses and ethical considerations concerned with genetic engineering.

USE

May be used as extension work on glucose in the blood, on hormones, and as an example of genetic engineering.

ADAPTING THE UNIT

☐ The BBC Radio programme may be used to provide background information about diabetes as an introduction to the unit. It describes the life of Sarah, a young diabetic person whose life depends on insulin; best heard while looking at the first page of the unit.

☐ The introductory information may be set as a homework exercise.

☐ A more active approach is to provide students with an enlarged Figure 3 on thin card so that they can cut out and insert the gene to model the process.

☐ Groups may be allocated different discussion points and asked to report back after 5 minutes.

☐ Some teachers extend the unit to deal with the problems of people living with diabetes.

OTHER RESOURCES

An ICI poster and notes on genetic engineering provides illustrated details of this technique.

NEW MATERIAL

Paragraph three on page 1 implies that insulin controls the transfer of glucose in and out of the liver. This is inaccurate. Insulin promotes the cellular uptake of glucose and biosynthetic processes only. A revised paragraph three for page 1 is provided. It may be stuck over the old paragraph but will extend into the white space beside it.

First published 1986

Replacement for paragraph three on page 1

- CUT - - - -

Insulin is the hormone which lowers the level of glucose in the blood by increasing the transport of glucose into cells. It is made in the pancreas, just below the stomach. From the pancreas insulin passes into the bloodstream and hence to the liver. Insulin is needed for the conversion of glucose to glycogen in the liver.

Insulin is normally secreted in response to food. If people do not produce insulin they cannot store or use glucose. Glucose then builds up in the bloodstream and some is lost in the urine. This happens in insulin-dependent diabetes mellitus.

- -

CUT

Recycling Aluminium

<table>
<tr><td>

Science content

Aluminium in domestic waste, recycling, non-renewable resource, electrolysis.

Science curriculum links
AT5   Human influences on the earth
AT7   Making new materials

Syllabus links
  ○ GCSE Science, Chemistry

Cross-curricular themes
  ○ Economic Awareness

Lesson time
  1 hour with prior homework

</td></tr>
</table>

<table>
<tr><td>

Links with other SATIS materials
410   Glass
604   Metals as Resources
1010   Can it be done?
       (question 16)
1106   Tin Cans

NERIS
Search on
       ALUMINIUM
  or   RECYCLING and UPPER
       SECONDARY

</td></tr>
</table>

STUDENT ACTIVITIES

☐ Home survey (data gathering): estimating aluminium use in the home.

☐ Questions to answer and discuss (suitable for individual work or small groups): the economics of recycling.

☐ Quantitative calculations on the manufacture of aluminium by electrolysis (suitable for homework): the high cost of electricity in making aluminium.

USE

May be used to follow work on the extraction and uses of metals.

Page 3 is suitable for able students late in the fifth year and may be omitted. It provides an extension to quantitative work on electrolysis and has been successfully used for A-level chemistry as an exercise on moles.

ADAPTING THE UNIT

☐ If students omit page 3, the point needs to be made to them that energy costs are a major component of the cost of making aluminium. Electricity accounts for about 25 per cent of the cost of aluminium in the UK. The energy cost of recycling aluminium is only 5 per cent of the energy cost of newly manufactured metal.

☐ An alternative is for students to collect all the aluminium they throw away in a week at home. Clean it (by soaking in detergent with a little bleach), let it dry and bring it into school. The calculations can then be shared by the class.

UPDATING INFORMATION

There is only one minor change in cost and most teachers may not consider it necessary to adjust the calculations.

☐ *For page 2, question 3 and for page 3* The price of aluminium in 1990 was £940 per tonne.

☐ *For page 3 (g)* The cost of electricity to aluminium manufacturers in 1990 remains at 3p a unit. (This is because some aluminium manufacturers produce their own electricity for less than 3p a unit and even sell the excess to the National Grid.)

First published 1986

Fluoridation of Water Supplies

Science content

Teeth, fluoride ion, water supplies

Science curriculum links
AT3   Processes of life
AT5   Human influences on the Earth

Syllabus links
○   GCSE Science, Biology, Chemistry

Cross-curricular themes
○   Health Education

Lesson time
1 hour
(homework possible)

Links with other SATIS materials
606   Tristan da Cunha Dental Surveys
1104   Materials to Repair Teeth
607   Scale and Scum
801   The Water Pollution Mystery
1010   Can it be done? (questions 14, 24)

NERIS
Search on
FLUORIDATION
and ROLE-PLAY

STUDENT ACTIVITIES

☐ Reading and questions, analyzing graphs: regions with less tooth decay, experimental fluoridation of water supplies, the fluoridation issue, other ways to get fluoride.

☐ Completing an opinion grid (working in pairs).

☐ Discussion points.

USE

May be used as extension work on teeth, water and the halogens. Part 1 is suitable for individual study or homework.

This unit may be used to follow SATIS 606, *The Tristan da Cunha Dental Surveys*.

ADAPTING THE UNIT

☐ Using Part 2, the opinion grid, as a data-gathering exercise. Students have had family and friends complete copies of the sheet for the class to analyze.

☐ Using the topic in a formal debate.

☐ Doing a toothpaste survey.

☐ Using the new student material.

UPDATING INFORMATION

☐ *The Teachers' Notes, under General Notes, point 1* should include a third compound used in fluoridation, *sodium fluoride*, NaF.

☐ Young children who swallow toothpaste instead of rinsing it out take in about 0.5 mg of fluoride a day.

☐ *For the bottom line of page 3*, the cost of filling one decayed tooth varies between £5 and £15, with an average of about £6.50 in 1990.

NEW MATERIAL

☐ Making a time chart.

☐ Transferring the data from Figure 3 to the dental charts.

☐ Producing a 'fluoridation page' for a newspaper.

First published 1986

Q1   The unit gives several dates. Produce a time chart, with the dates and what happened. (However, be careful, the story is not told in the order it unfolded!) Include the Second World War; its dates were 1939 to 1945.

Q2   For this question, use results of dental surveys, page 3, figure 3.

The teeth on the dental charts below each have 10 divisions. Use each division to represent 100 decayed, missing or filled teeth (DMF). Transfer the data from the graphs to the dental charts.

Share the work with a partner, one of you doing the charts for the upper jaw, the other for the lower jaw.

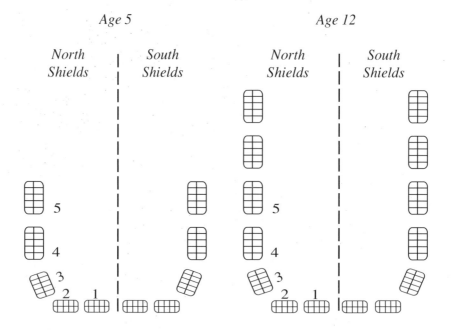

Q3   In recent years figures for the number of decayed, missing or filled teeth in children have been falling whether the water supply has a high fluoride content or not. Why do you think this is so?

Q4   Imagine your group are reporters on the staff of a local newspaper. You have just discovered that artificial fluoridation of your local water supplies was secretly started last week.

Produce a 'page' for the newspaper with:

● 'articles' for and against the fluoridation of the water supply,

● 'interviews' with local dignitaries, pensioners, children whose goldfish have died etc,

● 'letters' from local residents and dentists,

● editorial comment.

DDT and Malaria

Science content

Infective organism, life cycle of parasite, insecticide, food chain, predator-prey relationships, ecosystem.

Science curriculum links
AT 2   The variety of life
AT 3   Processes of life
AT 5   Human influences on the Earth

Syllabus links
○   GCSE Science, Biology, Chemistry

Cross-curricular themes
○   Health Education
○   Environment

Lesson time
    1½ hours
    (homework possible)

Links with other SATIS materials
210   The Pesticide Problem
304   A Medicine to Control Bilharzia

BBC Radio SATIS Topics 14–16
    DDT and Malaria

NERIS
Search on
        MALARIA
or   PESTICIDES
        and UPPER SECONDARY

STUDENT ACTIVITIES

☐   Reading and answering questions: malaria, the life cycle of the malarial parasite, DDT an insecticide, the food chain.

☐   Reading and answering questions: Operation Cat Drop describes how DDT disturbed an ecosystem in Borneo.

☐   Points for discussion: may be done with students working in small groups and reporting back. Groups can be allocated different questions.

USE

May be used to illustrate a way in which human activity has affected the environment. It describes how a persistent chemical can be passed along a food chain and the ecological effect of removing members of the food chain.

ADAPTING THE UNIT

☐   The BBC Radio programme describes the problems of malaria and forms a good introduction to the unit. It is probably best used to enhance the first page of the unit.

☐   The main part of the unit could be set for homework or independent study, with a class or group discussion to round off the work.

☐   Less able students may be helped by discussing the meaning of the technical terminology or by making a glossary before they read the unit.

☐   Comprehension questions are provided in the new material. They relate to pages 1 and 2 and the BBC Radio programme.

FURTHER INFORMATION

DDT is still widely used, particularly in South America. Pyrethrum, mentioned on page 5 and in Teachers' Notes (i) is not widely used because it is very unstable to light. Synthetic analogues of pyrethrum, the photostable synthetic pyrethroids are nearly ideal insecticides.

NEW MATERIAL

☐   Information about malaria for travellers.

☐   Questions about pages 1 and 2 of the student sheets.

☐   Questions relating to the BBC Radio programme.

First published 1986

Can you catch malaria?

More than 2000 people a year come back to Britain with malaria caught on holiday or from working abroad. A few die.

Malaria occurs in Africa, Asia and South America. As yet, there is no vaccine against it. Anti-malarial drugs exist but are too expensive for ordinary people in the developing world. To make matters worse, the malarial parasite has become resistant to most of the drugs that in the past were used to treat it.

Anybody travelling to an area where there is malaria should seek medical advice before going. Types of malaria differ and travellers need to take anti-malarial pills that are effective in the region they visit. Even so, they should try to avoid being bitten by mosquitoes.

The BBC Radio programme tells you more about it.

The following questions are about pages 1 and 2 of the student sheets, the information on this page and the BBC Radio programme.

> *Q1*   *How can you catch malaria?*
>
> *Q2*   *What is an insecticide?*
>
> *Q3*   *Malaria is caused by a parasite. Explain what this is.*
>
> *Q4*   *If you had malaria, what symptoms would you have?*
>
> *Q5*   *Where does the malarial parasite,* Plasmodium, *live and reproduce?*
>
> *Q6*   *Explain how controlling the population of mosquitoes is an effective way of preventing malaria.*

If you listened to the BBC Radio tape:

> *Q7*   *Where did Andrew Vardon catch malaria?*
>
> *Q8*   *Has he been permanently cured?*
>
> *Q9*   *From your understanding of the life cycle of the malarial parasite, explain why travellers should continue to take anti-malarial pills for at least four weeks on their return.*

In 1955, with no vaccine against malaria and no drugs that ordinary people could afford, the World Health Organisation decided to wipe out malaria by killing the mosquitoes that spread it. The story in the unit tells what happened.

Britain's Energy Sources

Science content

Primary and secondary energy sources, energy transfer and efficiency.

Science curriculum links
AT13 Energy

Syllabus links
- GCSE Science, Physics
- Geography

Cross-curricular themes
- Economic Awareness

Lesson time
1–2 hours
(following a home survey)

Links with other SATIS materials

109	Nuclear Power
601	Electricity on Demand
701	Electricity in your Home
702	The Gas Supply Problem
980	Why not Combined Heat and Power?

NERIS
Search on
    ENERGY SOURCES
and STATISTICAL DATA
or   COSTS

or on
    ENERGY CONSUMPTION
and STATISTICAL DATA
or   COSTS

STUDENT ACTIVITIES

☐ Introduction.

☐ Home survey and answering questions: what sources of energy are used at home, the costs.

☐ Data analysis: comparing the sorts of energy sources.

☐ Reading and answering questions: why electricity is expensive.

☐ Reading and answering questions: the major energy users.

USE

As part of a study of harnessing energy sources. The unit focuses on use in the home and broadens to consider major end users. Mathematical skills are needed to cope with some of the questions.

ADAPTING THE UNIT

☐ The numbers may be simplified for less able students.

☐ The teacher needs to be prepared with data for students who have not done their initial home survey!

☐ Use parts of the unit only. Part 2 is probably the most useful part on its own.

☐ Use as the basis for an 'energy in the home' project.

NEW MATERIAL

Table 2 and Table 6 have been updated to 1989 figures and are reprinted overleaf.

The UK Energy Statistics Card is available free. The address is now: Department of Energy, 1 Palace Street, London SW1E 5HE.

New answers

Q 5   *Based on 1989 figures, the answer is*

	Energy in MJ for £1
Coal	300
Fuel oil	307
Gas	244
Electricity	65

Q14   *The 1989 figure for amount of coal used per year was 2835 billion MJ. (This figure is only slightly less than the figure given for 1983.) Most was used for generating electricity (2458 billion MJ).*

Q15   *(The proportion of nuclear generated electricity remains the same.)*

First published 1986

Table 2   *Costs of different energy sources*

Energy source	Unit in which you buy it	Cost of one unit	Amount bought for £1
Coal	tonne (1000 kg)	£100	10 kg
Fuel oil	litre	£ 0.12	8.3 litres
Mains gas	therm	£ 0.43	2.3 therms
Electricity	kilowatt-hour (kWh)	£ 0.055	18 kWh

Table 6   *Final users of different energy sources. The figures are in billions of megajoules per year (1 billion megajoules = 10^{15} J). They apply to the year 1989.*

	Coal	Oil	Gas	Electricity
Industry	198	399	568	320
Road transport	—	1529	—	—
Domestic	151	94	1046	332
Other	28	574	297	285
Total	377	2596	1911	937

How would you Survive?

Science content

Survival, food, water, shelter, clothing, energy, appropriate technology.

Science curriculum links
AT 2 The variety of life
AT 5 Human influences on the Earth

Syllabus links
○ GCSE Science, Biology, Chemistry, Physics
○ Geography
○ Sixth-form General Studies
○ Technology

Cross-curricular themes
○ Health Education
○ Environment

Lesson time
1–2 hours

Links with other SATIS materials
107   Ashton Island
708   Appropriate Pumps
802   Hypothermia
803   The Technology of Toilets
806   Stress
905   The Impact of IT
1006 As Safe as Houses

STUDENT ACTIVITIES

For students working in pairs

☐ A task exercise: survival when shipwrecked in the arctic – food, water, shelter, clothing, fire.

☐ Discussion questions: appropriate technology.

USE

May be used to bring a personal perspective to the issues involving human influences on the Earth, with work on (human) adaptation to environment, with energy and with testing the insulating properties of clothing. The unit has also been used for fifth year PSE classes.

Part 2 may be linked to other SATIS units about appropriate technology.

A very popular unit with all ages and abilities because everyone can contribute ideas and suggestions. Although the tasks are designed for pairs, Part 2 may be answered individually.

The unit provides a context with numerous design opportunities for technology.

ADAPTING THE UNIT

☐ Some teachers shorten and restructure the list on page 4.

☐ The unit has been used as a practical assignment, providing students with raw materials to create a shelter and make food in the school playground!

☐ A new worksheet for page 3 is provided for less able students.

NEW MATERIAL

A worksheet for page 3.

First published 1986

Your name

Task 1

The resources you would have are

Task 3
Which would work?

Task 2

Food	*What would you eat?*	
	How would you catch it?	
	How would you cook?	

| Water | *How would you get drinking water?* | |

Shelter	*What kind of shelter would you build?*	
	What materials would you use?	
	What tools would you use?	

| Clothing | *How would you make clothing?* | |
| | *Bedding?* | |

| Fire | *How would you start it?* | |
| | *How would you keep it going?* | |

The Label at the Back

Science content

Natural, synthetic and regenerated fibres, commercial polymers and their manufacture.

Science curriculum links
AT 1 Exploration of science
AT 6 Types and uses of materials
AT 7 Making new materials

Syllabus links
○ GCSE Science, Chemistry
○ Sixth-form General Studies
○ Technology (fabrics)

Lesson time
   1–2 hours
   (with prior homework)

Links with other SATIS materials
104 What's in our Food?
910 Disposable Nappies
1010 Can it be done?
     (question 18)

NERIS
Search on
      TEXTILES and CLOTHING
Additional search terms
      TEXTILE FIBRES

STUDENT ACTIVITIES

☐ Survey, data gathering (at home or at school): clothes labels – fibre content and country of origin.

☐ Data handling.

☐ Data presentation and evaluation.

☐ Questions: fibres, chemical structures, cost.

USE

May be used as part of a study of materials or as an introduction or extension to work on polymers. Factsheet 3 is intended for able students only.

ADAPTING THE UNIT

☐ Factsheet 3 is frequently omitted.

☐ The other factsheets may be simplified with the awesome words and chemical formulas removed.

UPDATING INFORMATION

☐ Figure 2 shows an example of dry spinning. Wet spinning and melt spinning are also used.

☐ There are several types of nylon and polyester, only one example of each is given on Factsheet 3.

☐ 'Acetate' is in fact 'diacetate'. A corrected structural formula is given below. It may be patched over the original on the master, or the extra 'Ac' groups marked on Factsheet 3.

Monomer   *Structure of part of the polymer*

glucose diacetate

First published 1986

Blindness

Science content

Function of the eye, causes of blindness.

Science curriculum links
AT15 Using light and electromagnetic radiation

Syllabus links
○ GCSE Science, Biology

Cross-curricular themes
○ Health Education
○ Citizenship

Lesson time
    1 hour

Links with other SATIS materials
209   Spectacles and Contact Lenses
1010 Can it be done? (question 19)
1102 A Special Type of Hearing Aid

BBC Radio SATIS topics 14–16
    Blindness

NERIS
Search on
    BLINDNESS and HUMAN BIOLOGY

STUDENT ACTIVITIES

☐ Activity and questions: a blindfolded walk.

☐ Reading and questions to answer or discuss: structure of the eye, causes of blindness, blindness in tropical countries.

USE

May be used as extension work on the eye and senses. It has been useful in PSE.

ADAPTING THE UNIT

☐ Omit questions 9, 10 and 11 with less able students.

☐ Have students test themselves on eye charts with 'partial sight' by wearing worn and scratched goggles. Use goggles with colour filters to simulate the experience of colour deficiencies.

☐ Show an out of focus image with a slide projector and have students guess what it is.

☐ The BBC Radio programme, 'Blindness', provides excellent support for this unit. It is best used along with page 1, after students have simulated blindness for themselves. The programme takes you out on a walk with Peter White, a blind radio journalist, accompanied by the presenter, John Gribbin.

☐ Collect bottles with braille labelling, e.g. bleach and white spirit.

☐ Use braille or Moon cards available from the RNIB.

UPDATING INFORMATION

☐ The Royal Commonwealth Society for the Blind is now called Sight Savers. [Teachers' Notes (ii)]

☐ The Royal National Institute for the Blind (RNIB) will supply information on visual impairment, including samples of braille sheets. The Royal National Institute for the Blind Community Education Office is at 224 Great Portland Street, London W1N 6AA. Tel. 071-388 1266.

UPDATING MATERIAL

Additions and amendments are provided overleaf.

First published 1986

> *The following are amendments to update and enhance the student material.*
>
> *It is suggested that a copy of the page is made. The replacement paragraphs may be glued over the originals on the masters, or copied and stuck onto the student sheets.*
>
> *The minor amendments may be made directly to the sheets.*

Page 1, paragraph one.

-          CUT

For those of us who can see, it is difficult to imagine what it would be like to be blind. *But more than 40 million people in the world are blind*, many millions more are partially sighted. With a world population of over 4 billion, that is one in every hundred people.

-          CUT

-          CUT

Blindness in Britain

In Britain nearly one million people are visually impaired, that is partially sighted or blind. Blindness is most common among older people. The main causes of blindness and partial sight are macular degeneration, diabetes, glaucoma and cataracts.

Macular degeneration is a disorder of the retina at the back of the eye. This is the part of the eye where light-sensitive rod cells convert light into an electrical signal for the brain.

Diabetes can cause blood vessels in the eye to grow abnormally. The vessels may weaken and spill blood on the retina. If this problem is discovered early, a surgeon can reseal the blood vessels by welding them with a fine laser beam.

Glaucoma is caused by a build up of pressure in the aqueous humour of the eye. An optician normally checks for it in older people as part of a routine eye test.

Only 4 per cent of blind people are totally blind. In Britain people are registered blind if they are unable to read the top letter in an eyesight test from three metres or less. People with 'partial sight' do not see very well but have enough sight to read and write. What each person sees depends on his or her condition.

-          CUT

Page 3, Cataracts, second paragraph, please insert

The blindness can be cured by removing the lens *and replacing it with an artificial one*.

Page 4, question 5

You may wish the change the term 'sticks' to '*canes*', if students are familiar with the term.

Noise

Science content

Loudness, decibel scale, sources of noise, effects on health, noise control in the environment.

Science curriculum links
AT14 Sound and music

Syllabus links
○ GCSE Science, Biology, Physics
○ Sixth-form General Studies
○ Technology

Cross-curricular themes
○ Health Education
○ Environment
○ Citizenship

Lesson time
1 hour or more
(homework possible)

Links with other SATIS materials
903 What are the Sounds of Music?
1102 A Special Type of Hearing Aid

BBC Radio SATIS topics 14–16
Noise

NERIS
Search on
NOISE CONTROL

STUDENT ACTIVITIES

☐ Reading and answering questions: noise, decibel scale; sources of noise.

☐ Interpreting graphical data: evidence of effect of noise on health.

☐ Reading and answering questions: noise reduction.

☐ Opinion survey: noise in your school.

USE

The material has been used along with work on the ear in biology and on sound in physics. An enjoyable 'low decibel unit', which is suitable for all abilities!

ADAPTING THE UNIT

☐ The BBC Radio programme, 'Noise', provides material which supports this unit. It describes how workers in industry are protected from exposure to excessive noise. The programme could best be used at the end of Part 2 or Part 4.

☐ The survey may be omitted if time is short. However, students find it particularly rewarding.

☐ Practical work may be added if a noise meter is available.

☐ Teacher discussion of the interpretation of the graphs on page 5 may be aided by making OHP masters with overlays from the student sheets.

☐ The summary of the Opinion Survey has been sent as a letter to the headteacher.

☐ Students could investigate the effect of noise on carrying out a complex task near a very loud noise source (if you can find somewhere to do it!).

OTHER RESOURCES

The Noise at Work Regulations 1989, HMSO.

First published 1986

Industrial Gases

Science content

Oxygen, nitrogen, hydrogen, argon, helium, properties, manufacture.

Science curriculum links
AT 6   Types and uses of
          materials

Syllabus links
   ○   GCSE Science, Chemistry

Cross-curricular themes
   ○   Economic Awareness

Lesson time
        1½hours
        (homework possible)

Links with other SATIS materials
207   The Story of Fritz Haber
301   Air Pollution
810   High Pressure Chemistry
902   Acid Rain

STUDENT ACTIVITIES

☐ Data searching: looking up the properties of five gases.

☐ Reading and answering questions: industrial uses.

USE

This unit is suitable for revision of the properties of gases. Successful for self-study. Links with modules on 'the air'.

ADAPTING THE UNIT

☐ Part 1 and Part 2 may be used separately.

☐ Some teachers add carbon dioxide and ammonia to the list of gases.

UPDATING INFORMATION

The total volumes of gases consumed have changed very little over the years and prices have remained much the same. With new technology and efficiency improvements the industry has remained profitable. The number of production locations shown in *Figure 3* has been increased to 14.

First published 1986

Dam Problems

Science content

Hydroelectric power, extraction of aluminium, rain forest, desert, savanna, malaria, wildlife, fisheries, land use, soil erosion, local people.

Science curriculum links
AT5   Human influences on the Earth
AT13 Energy

Syllabus links
○ GCSE Science, Biology
○ Geography
○ Sixth-form General Studies
○ Social Biology

Cross-curricular themes
○ Environment
○ Citizenship

Lesson time
1–2 hours
(following homework preparation)

Links with other SATIS materials
402   DDT and Malaria
304   A Medicine to Control Bilharzia – Part 1.

502   The Coal Mine Project
602   The Limestone Inquiry
605   The Great Chunnel Debate

BBC Radio SATIS Topics 14–16
Dam Problems

SATIS Audiovisual
Dams, People and the Environment

NERIS
Search on
ENVIRONMENTAL IMPACT and HYDROELECTRIC POWER
or on
ENVIRONMENTAL IMPACT and RAIN FORESTS

STUDENT ACTIVITIES

☐ Preparation for role-play: the scenario is a proposal for a hydro-electric dam in an imaginary country; three possible sites: rain forest, desert, savanna.

☐ Role-play in groups of eight or nine: the Minister of Energy, a Sociologist, an Ecologist, a Land Use Consultant.

☐ Completing an Environmental Impact Assessment table.

USE

May be used to highlight the economic and environmental costs of using an energy source (hydroelectric power) and to provide an opportunity for students to argue for and against a planning proposal with an environmental impact.

Works well with all-ability classes and is very popular. 'The arguments continued long after the bell.'

ADAPTING THE UNIT

☐ The BBC Radio programme accompanies the General Briefing sheets. It sets the scene by 'painting pictures in the mind', filling out descriptions of the sites illustrated on page GB2. Questions are provided in the new material.

☐ The SATIS Audiovisual programme, *Dams, People and the Environment*, has some useful slides (numbers 4, 7, 8, 11, 12, 14, 17 and 20) which could help students to visualise the situation.

☐ Although the Teachers' Notes suggest two students per role, classroom experience suggests that three students for the role of Minister of Energy works better. Have the three elect a spokesperson, with the other two acting as consultants during the role-play.

☐ Allow students plenty of time to read the briefings and to formulate their policies together.

☐ Figure 3 could be enlarged and made into an OHP transparency for presenting the problem to the class.

☐ Less able students can be asked to colour a copy of the map, Figure 3, to familiarize themselves with the problem. A map and colouring suggestions are provided.

NEW MATERIAL

A 'consumable' page to link with the General Briefing material, containing a copy of the map, colouring suggestions and questions related to the BBC Radio programme.

First published 1986

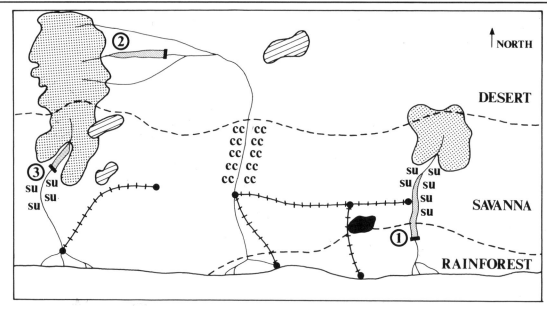

KEY ①▬▶ Proposed dam & flooded area   ⬿ River
                                         ⬿ Railway   SCALE
     ● Bauxite deposits   ● Town   ├────┤
     ⬭ National Parks   **su** Main areas of subsistence farming   APPROX 100 km
     ⬚ High ground   **cc** Main areas of cash crops

Colouring the map

On the map of the proposed sites for the dam, colour the
- sea – *blue*
- rivers and proposed flooded areas – *blue*
- national parks – *green*
- high ground – *brown*

Add these colours to the key.

Shade the vegetation zones with different colours or patterns. Keep this shading pale so that it does not hide the other features of the map.

Questions on the BBC Radio programme

Site 1 Forest
F1   *What people live in the rainforest?*
F2   *What would be lost by felling the forest to make a dam?*
F3   *What would happen to the fish further down river?*

Site 2 Desert
D1   *Describe the climate of this desert.*
D2   *What is an oasis?*
D3   *Why might the dam silt up?*

Site 3 Savanna
S1   *Describe the savanna landscape.*
S2   *Making a lake in this region may bring mosquitoes. What disease can they spread?*
S3   *What would need to be done to protect the special plant found growing in the area?*

Q1   *Which sites for the dam would require the resettlement of local people?*
Q2   *How would a dam change local agriculture at each site?*
Q3   *Before you discuss these issues with others, which do you think is more important –*
          conservation, protecting people or profit?

Glass

Science content

Materials, glass, everyday use, manufacture, recycling.

Science curriculum links

AT 5   Human influences on the Earth

AT 6   Types and uses of materials

Syllabus links
○   GCSE Science, Chemistry
○   Technology

Cross-curricular themes
○   Environment

Lesson time
   1 hour

Links with other SATIS materials

310   Recycling Aluminium
1010   Can it be done?
          (question 15)
1106   Tin Cans

NERIS
Search on
          GLASS

STUDENT ACTIVITIES

☐ Demonstration (optional – details in the Teachers' Notes): making glass in the laboratory.

☐ Reading and answering questions: uses of glass, how glass is made, recycling, shaping glass, glass sheets, special kinds of glass.

USE

May be used to complement work on materials, carbonates, to illustrate the uses of raw materials and recycling. Suitable for most abilities.

ADAPTING THE UNIT

☐ This unit may be linked to other work on recycling.

☐ Students can investigate the amount of waste glass produced by their homes per week. (See SATIS 310, *Recycling Aluminium*.)

FURTHER INFORMATION

Although Pyrosil and Pyrex are linked together as heat resistant glasses in the text on page 4, Pyrosil is really a heat resistant glass ceramic. Glass ceramics are an expanding area of interesting materials.

An alternative recipe for demonstrating glass making is

sodium (hexa) metaphosphate	7.5 g
boron phosphate	1.0 g
barium hydrogen orthophosphate	1.5 g

The barium phosphate is toxic, but not as volatile as the lead oxide and only a little is used.

First published 1986

Bridges

Science content

Bridge structures, forces, tension, compression, bending, materials.

Science curriculum links
AT10 Forces

Syllabus links
○ GCSE Science, Physics
○ Technology

Lesson time
1–4 hours

Links with other SATIS materials
1006 As Safe as Houses
1009 Trees as Structures
1010 Can it be done?
(question 20)

SATIS Audiovisual
Bridges

NERIS
Search on
BRIDGES and DESIGN
or CONSTRUCTION

STUDENT ACTIVITIES

☐ Survey and classify: bridge types and materials (from local survey or from photographs).

☐ Information and questions: structural principles.

☐ Information and questions: material considerations.

☐ Design, build and test: briefs for a 25 cm span bridge, a 50 cm span bridge of maximum mass 30 g.

USE

The material links with Key Stage 3 of the Technology National Curriculum. Liaison with the technology department is suggested. In science it may be used as introductory or extension work on forces. The unit is suitable for all abilities but more appropriate for Key Stage 3. Students enjoy the unit, especially surveying local bridges. A good holiday project.

ADAPTING THE UNIT

☐ The SATIS Audiovisual, *Bridges*, provides slides and a well-paced commentary to enhance the material of the unit. It is suitable for a wide range of students from second to fifth form.

☐ There are possibilities for developing this topic into a cross-curricular project involving science, technology and history.

☐ The design task has been used for GCSE assessed practical work, the student brief allowing 20 minutes for planning, 30 minutes for construction and 20 minutes for evaluation.

OTHER RESOURCES

☐ BBC TV Science in Action programme for schools, 'Bridging the gap'.

☐ Gordon, J. E., *The Science of Structures and Materials*, Scientific American Library, (1988), ISBN 0 7167 5022 8.

First published 1986

The Coal Mine Project

Science content

Energy, carbon chemistry, conservation,

Science curriculum links
AT5   Human influences on the Earth
AT7   Making new materials
AT13 Energy

Syllabus links
○   GCSE Science, Chemistry
○   Geography
○   Sixth-form General Studies

Cross-curricular themes
○   Environment
○   Citizenship

Lesson time
1–2 hours
(following homework preparation)

Links with other SATIS materials
109   Nuclear Power
403   Britain's Energy Sources
1001 Chocolate Chip Mining.

BBC Radio SATIS Topics 14–16
The Coal Mine Project

NERIS
Search on
COAL MINING
or on
COAL MINING and
PHYSICAL PLANNING or
ENVIRONMENTAL IMPACT

STUDENT ACTIVITIES

☐ Preparation for role-play (mostly homework): the scenario – a proposed coal mine in the locality. (Teachers will need to provide a local map and select a site.)

☐ Role play: 13 roles for a simulated public meeting.

☐ The audience has an opinion grid to complete.

USE

May be used to complement work on fossil fuels, to help students identify the positive and negative effects of the exploitation of coal as a raw material and as a fossil fuel.

This is a very popular unit with students and has been successfully used with the third form.

ADAPTING THE UNIT

☐ The BBC Radio programme tells how students prepared themselves for this role-play exercise. It would be best heard when students receive the general briefing and their role-play cards.

First published 1986

Paying for National Health

Science content

Heart disease, health education, kidney disease, drug dependence, intensive care for new-born babies, geriatric care, hip replacement, AIDS.

Science curriculum links
AT 3 Processes of life

Syllabus links
- GCSE Science, Biology
- Sixth-form General Studies
- Technology

Cross-curricular themes
- Health Education
- Citizenship
- Economic Awareness

Lesson time
    1–2 hours
    (homework preparation)

Links with other SATIS materials
Medical:
206   Test Tube Babies
302   Living with Kidney Failure
506   Materials for Life
603   The Heart Pacemaker
1010 Can it be done?
      (questions 19, 22, 35, 39)

Citizenship awareness:
605   The Great Chunnel Debate
808   Should we Build a Fallout
      Shelter?
507   Computers and Jobs

SATIS 16–19
7   Kidney transplants
24   X-rays and patients

NERIS
Search on
      NATIONAL HEALTH
      SERVICE
or on
      HEALTH SERVICES and
      COSTS

STUDENT ACTIVITIES

☐ Reading the General Briefing (possible homework): a Health District budget.

☐ Preparation of cases by the interest groups: briefing sheets are provided on eight health topics.

☐ Structured discussion and decision-making.

USE

This unit would be useful for the revision of many aspects of health and human biology. It is a demanding unit, suitable for able students or sixth-form general studies. The format of a decision-making exercise presents students with a wide variety of information in a very interesting and economical way.

ADAPTING THE UNIT

☐ The unit is structured so that it may be used in a variety of ways as suggested in the Teachers' Notes.

UPDATING AND FURTHER INFORMATION

☐ With the reform of the Health Service, District Health Authorities will be making the kind of choices in the unit in a more explicit manner than before. They are now responsible for purchasing health services for their resident population.

☐ The unit remains up-to-date except that the costs should be increased by about 50 per cent for 1990.

☐ Erratum for Sheet B1: the sub-heading should read:

'(a) Heart Attack Response Team'

First published 1986

How Safe is your Car?

Science content

Force, mass, acceleration, kinetic energy.

Science curriculum links
AT10 Forces
AT13 Energy

Syllabus links
○ GCSE Science, Physics

Cross-curricular themes
○ Citizenship

Lesson time
1–2 hours
(homework possible)

Links with other SATIS materials
203 Drinking Alcohol
705 Physics in Playgrounds
1010 Can it be done?
    (Question 21)

BBC Radio SATIS Topics 14–16
How Safe is your Car?

NERIS
Search on
    BRAKING
or on
    BRAKING DISTANCES
Additional search terms
    SEAT BELTS
    MOTOR CARS and SAFETY
    ENGINEERING

STUDENT ACTIVITIES

☐ Reading and answering questions: the MOT test, stopping distances and safety, seat belts and accidents.

USE

The unit is best used for revision of forces and motion.

ADAPTING THE UNIT

☐ Part 1 works well as homework. It involves the whole family.

☐ Less able students may need to discuss the meaning of the questions before attempting them since the MOT is couched in 'adult' language.

☐ The BBC Radio programme accompanies a young motorist who has recently passed her driving test. It considers the problems of driving and estimating distances, like the 2 second rule. The programme goes on to consider stopping distances in different conditions. Probably best used at the start of Part 2 of the unit.

☐ Less able students could omit question 9 and paragraphs 2 and 3 of page 3.

☐ Students could be given a completed MOT form and asked to suggest what was wrong with the car.

FURTHER INFORMATION

Perceived risk analysis suggests that motorists drive faster and take more risks now that seat belts are compulsory. The class might like to consider what evidence might justify this point of view.

There are plans to introduce the testing of exhaust gases.

In 1990 the cost of the MOT was £15.50. The MOT check list, Figure 2, in the unit remains the same (at the time of updating).

NEW MATERIAL

☐ The new Highway Code gives stopping distances in imperial and metric units.

☐ Some of the laws regarding the condition of motor vehicles for comparison with the MOT test.

First published 1986

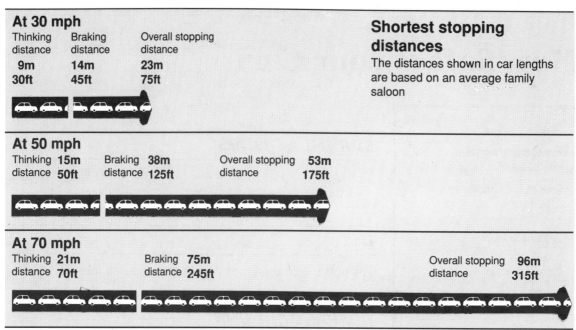

New Figure 4 Shortest stopping distances (from the Highway Code 1987 edition)

Below are some of the requirements of the law relating to cars from page 67 of the Highway Code. (They have been edited to shorten them.)

Before driving you must make sure that

☐ the condition of your vehicle, of any trailer it is drawing and of any load, and the number of passengers and the way in which they are carried, are such that they do not endanger yourself or others

☐ your brakes and steering are in good working order and properly adjusted

☐ your tyres are suitable for the vehicle, are properly inflated, have a continuous tread depth of at least 1 mm across three quarters of the width, with visible tread across the remainder of the width, and are free from cuts and other defects

☐ your windscreen and other windows are free from obstruction to vision; are kept clean; wipers and washers should be maintained in effective working order at all times

☐ your seat belts, anchorages, fastenings and adjusting devices are maintained free from obvious defects

☐ your vehicle is fitted with the appropriate number of mirrors, so fitted that you can see traffic behind you

☐ your horn is in working order

☐ your exhaust system is efficient

☐ any audible anti-theft device that may be fitted complies with the regulations

☐ the load on your vehicle is so secured that neither danger nor nuisance is caused by its falling or being blown off, or shifting

☐ your vehicle has lamps and reflectors which comply with the regulations and are in working order

☐ your headlamps are properly adjusted.

1   Discuss which requirements the MOT cannot test for.

2   These statements are very carefully worded. For instance, why must seat belts be free from obvious *defects? Pick out examples that with less precise wording might cause difficulties in applying the law.*

Making Fertilizers

Science content

Fertilizers in agriculture, raw materials for manufacture, environmental issues.

Science curriculum links
AT 1   Exploration of science
AT 2   The variety of life
AT 7   Making new materials

Syllabus links
○   GCSE Science,
     Chemistry,
○   Geography

Cross-curricular themes
○   Environment

Lesson time
     1 hour or more
     (homework possible)

Links with other SATIS materials
207   The Story of Fritz Haber
810   High Pressure Chemistry
1010   Can it be done?
       (question 27)
1201   Agrochemicals and the
       Environment

NERIS
Search on
       FERTILIZERS and UPPER
       SECONDARY

STUDENT ACTIVITIES

☐ Reading and answering questions: fertilizers and food production, the elements plants need, manufacture, problems with fertilizers.

☐ Planning and carrying out an experiment: making ammonium sulphate by neutralization.

☐ Testing the fertilizer: planning the investigation, setting up controls.

USE

May be used to enhance work on ammonia, fertilizers, food production and plant nutrition. Has been used as part of a soil module in geography. Suitable for most abilities and for use as homework (omitting page 5).

ADAPTING THE UNIT

☐ Some teachers report that the testing of the fertilizer does not work. Results can be disappointing if seeds are not allowed to grow well beyond the 'two leaf' stage.

Such experiments work best in spring or summer but need to be planned to avoid neglect during school holidays. (If such experiments are started in the autumn term, daylight hours shorten and the plants fail to thrive.) Wheat seeds perform well and some teachers report using mung beans which are very fast growing.

☐ Visits to fertilizer factories have added interest.

☐ Discussion may lead to sustainable and organic farming issues and the genetic engineering of nitrogen-fixing crops.

UPDATING INFORMATION

☐ *Page 1*   'Artificial' fertilizers may be more appropriately called 'manufactured'.

☐ *Page 2*   The fertilizers illustrated have been superseded.

☐ *Page 3 and Teachers' Notes (ii)* 'ICI Fertilizers', formerly the 'Agricultural Division' is no longer part of ICI.

First published 1986

Materials for Life

Science content

Medical technology, skeleton, artificial hip joints, suitable materials.

Science curriculum links

AT 3   Processes of life
AT 6   Types and uses of materials

Syllabus links

○   GCSE Science, Biology, Chemistry
○   Technology

Cross-curricular themes

○   Health Education

Lesson time

1–2 hours
(may be homework)

Links with other SATIS materials

302   Living with Kidney Failure
603   The Heart Pacemaker
707   Artificial Limbs

STUDENT ACTIVITIES

☐   Reading: information on replacement surgery, artificial hips, suitable materials.

☐   Questions relating to a case study: Kim needs an artificial hip joint.

USE

May be used to complement work on the human skeleton, on medical technology and on materials. This is a short unit and suitable for homework.

ADAPTING THE UNIT

☐   Normally done as it stands.

☐   Comprehension activities are provided for less able students.

☐   The discussion questions may be tackled in small groups with students electing a spokesperson to report back to the class.

☐   Interview relatives and friends who have had prostheses of any kind (bones pinned, dental bridges etc.). Find out what materials were used and what the prosthesis has done for them. Collect the information together – as a poster; write it up for the school magazine; produce an audio tape etc.

FURTHER INFORMATION

One of the long-term problems with major joint replacement remains loosening. Metallic implants are now being coated with a ceramic of calcium hydroxyapatite, which is a calcium phosphate and is the mineral of bone itself. This is a porous coating and encourages bone to attach and grow into it. Eventually it seems to be incorporated into the bone structure and therefore holds the implant firmly in place. The long-term durability is being studied.

New composite materials are also being made which incorporate hydroxyapatite in a plastic matrix material and show the same properties of bone conduction. Bioactive glasses containing phosphates are also being studied, as coatings or in composite materials.

NEW MATERIAL

Comprehension activities relating to pages 1, 2 and 3.

First published 1986

Questions about the diagrams and text

Q1   What is a ball and socket joint?

Q2   Give the common names for
   (a)   the pelvis,
   (b)   the femur.

Q3   What keeps the ball in the socket?

Q4   What reduces friction in a natural joint?

Q5   How is an artificial joint fixed into the bone?

Q6   Explain the advantages of using a ceramic for the ball part of the joint.

Q7   In the past, joints have tended to work loose. What is being tried to prevent this from happening?

Q8   Look through pages 1, 2 and 3. Copy the table headings.
   (a)   List in column one all the materials mentioned in the unit which are used for prostheses.
   (b)   Say what they are used for in column two.
   (c)   In column three write if they are metals, ceramics, glass, plastics and fibres or a combination of these materials.

   An example has been done for you.

Material	Used for	Type of material
metal amalgams	teeth fillings	metal

Computers and Jobs

Science content

Information handling, data processing, artificial intelligence.

Science curriculum links
AT12 IT including microelectronics

Syllabus links
○ GCSE Science, Physics
○ Sixth-form General Studies
○ Technology

Cross-curricular themes
○ Careers
○ Citizenship

Lesson time
1–2 hours

Links with other SATIS materials
905 The Impact of IT
1010 Can it be done? (questions 22, 26, 41)
1202 Mapping the Human Genome

NERIS
Search on
COMPUTER APPLICATION
and NEW TECHNOLOGY
and UPPER SECONDARY

STUDENT ACTIVITIES

☐ Brainstorming: comparing humans and computers (working in pairs).

☐ Case study and planning task: computerising the accounts department of 'Barnes Book Club' (working in pairs).

☐ Role-play (optional): management and workers.

☐ Discussion: computers, jobs and society.

☐ Story writing: the role of computers in 2020.

USE

For drawing together the applications of information technology and microelectronics and to provide an opportunity for the discussion of its implications for everyday life. This unit may be linked with the new SATIS unit, *Mapping the Human Genome*, a scientific project which depends heavily on computer technology.

Well suited to general studies or PSE. 'Stimulated much discussion'.

Links with Technology National Curriculum AT 5, Information technology capability.

First published 1986

Risks

Science content
Risk, life style and health (smoking, asbestos), nuclear power.
Science curriculum links AT3 Processes of life AT13 Energy
Syllabus links ○ GCSE Science, Biology, Physics ○ Sixth-form General Studies
Cross-curricular themes ○ Health Education ○ Environment ○ Citizenship
Lesson time 1–2 hours (some homework possible)

Links with other SATIS materials 109 Nuclear Power 203 Drinking Alcohol 807 Radiation – how much do you get? 909 AIDS 1002 Quintonal 1003 A Big Bang 1010 Can it be done? (questions 14, 24) **SATIS 16–19** 32 Risk **NERIS** Search on RISK ANALYSIS

STUDENT ACTIVITIES

☐ Reading, data handling and answering questions:

Part 1 Risks and how to calculate them

Part 2 Looking at particular risks

1 Dangerous substances, smoking and asbestos

2 Risks from nuclear power

☐ Discussion point for small groups: risks involved in different types of transport and occupational risks.

USE

The unit may be introduced in the context of work on the lungs and smoking or during work on energy and nuclear power.

As it stands, the unit is suitable for more able students. The new page provides alternative questions to make it accessible to a wider range of abilites.

ADAPTING THE UNIT

☐ If time is limited the unit may be used in parts, for example:

Parts 1 and 3 make a short topic on risks.

Part 2.1 extends work on the lungs into the risks of smoking and asbestos.

Part 2.2 extends work in harnessing nuclear power as a source of energy.

☐ Average students may need help with the terminology.

☐ Try the alternative questions provided.

UPDATING INFORMATION

Recent data on risks differs only slightly. The figures quoted in the unit are mutually consistent and do not require amendment.

The tolerability of risk from nuclear power stations, Health and Safety Executive, HMSO, 1988, £4.95, ISBN 0 11 883982 9, provides a very good discussion of risk assessment in general.

NEW MATERIAL

Extra page with alternative questions.

Your teacher may be able to tell you

(a) *how many students there are in your school. (If you do not have this information, assume the number is 1000.)*

(b) *how many students from your school have been killed in road traffic accidents in the past ten years.*

> ** Life-expectancy in the UK in the 1990s is about 78 years for women and 73 years for men. It is likely to increase. For you it should be about 81 years for women and 76 years for men.*

Questions on Part 1

Q1 *What do you think is riskier?*
(a) sleeping in bed, (b) crossing the road.

Q2 *(a) What is the risk of being killed in a road traffic accident per year?*
(b) The population of Birmingham is one million. How many people in Birmingham are likely to die from road traffic accidents in a year?

Q3 *(a) Work out the risk of someone from your school being killed in a road traffic accident during the year.*
(b) Does the number of students from your school killed on the roads differ from the national average? If so, suggest why this is.

Q4 *Look at the figures in Table 1. What are you most likely to die from during the coming year?*

Q5 *If you were a factory worker, would you be more likely to die from an accident at work or from one at home?*

Q6 *The figures in Table 1 are for annual risks of death. Suppose you live to be 80 years old*. What is your chance of being killed in an accident at home (this is your lifetime risk)?*

Question on Part 2.1

Q7 *You may die from being exposed to dangerous substances.*
(a) Which dangerous substances are named on pages 2 and 3?
(b) Why is it difficult to find out if substances are dangerous to health?

Q8 *If half the students in your school take up smoking 20 cigarettes a day, how many will die from it?*

Q9 *Unlike Table 1, the figures in Table 2 are for a lifetime risk. Suppose you spend 20 years of your life living in a building in which asbestos has been used as a building material.*
(a) What is your annual risk of death, assuming you live to 80*?
(b) How does this compare with the risk of being electrocuted at home? (See Table 1.)

Q10 *Suppose you have one million pounds to spend on reducing the risks in Table 2. What would you do with the money?*

Questions on Part 2.2

Since the Chernobyl accident, tens of thousands of children in the USSR have developed cancer, leukaemia and skin diseases.

The risk of a bad accident at a nuclear power plant with the release of radioactive material is now thought to be between 1 in 100 000 to 1 in 1 million per year. In other words, you would expect a bad accident at a particular nuclear power station about once in a million years or slightly more often.

> **Q11** *The risk of a bad nuclear accident at a particular nuclear power station in any year is certainly very low. There are some 400 nuclear power stations in the world. What is the risk of another bad accident like Chernobyl during your lifetime, say the next 60 years?*
>
> **Q12** *Nuclear power stations do not produce carbon dioxide, so they do not contribute to the greenhouse effect. Do you think it is better to run the risk of a nuclear accident than to add more carbon dioxide to the air from fossil fuel burning power stations?*

Homoeopathy

Science content

Medicines, fair tests, controls, data interpretation, scientific opinion and the uncertain nature of scientific proof.

Science curriculum links
AT1   Exploration of science
AT3   Processes of life
AT17 The nature of science

Syllabus links
○   GCSE Science, Biology
○   Sixth-form General Studies
○   Social Biology

Cross-curricular themes
○   Health Education

Lesson time
　　　1 hour

Links with other SATIS materials
305   A Medicine to Control Bilharzia
401   Fluoridation of Water Supplies
503   Paying for the National Health
703   Vegetarianism
805   The Search for the Magic Bullet

NERIS
Search on
　　　HOMOEOPATHY
or on
　　　ALTERNATIVE MEDICINE

STUDENT ACTIVITIES

☐ Reading, answering questions, data evaluation: the differences between homoeopathy and ordinary medicine, testing arthritis medicines.

☐ Discussion questions.

USE

May be used in association with work on disease. It shows how the efficacy of medicines is assessed.

ADAPTING THE UNIT

☐ Make a glossary of some of the terms used in this unit. For example *homoeopathy, medicine, vaccination, dilution, prescription, placebo, arthritis, course of treatment, paracetamol tablets.*

☐ Use the discussion points as the basis of a formal debate.

FURTHER INFORMATION

In 1988, the scientific journal, *Nature*, published a controversial article by Professor Benveniste which appeared to support the theory behind homoeopathic treatment. It reported that highly dilute solutions retained their activity even though no significant amount of solute could have been present.

As a result of protests from other scientists, *Nature* sent a team of investigators to Professor Benveniste's laboratories. (The team included a magician.) Their findings initially seemed to support the article, but were again disputed by other scientists.

Professor Benveniste's results have not been satisfactorily repeated elsewhere and are largely discredited. They have been variously ascribed to dirty apparatus, poor experimental procedure, especially to a lack of control experiments and to 'wishful thinking'. Professor Benveniste was suspended from his job a year later.

First published 1986

Perkin's Mauve

Science content

Dyes – natural and artificial.

Science curriculum links
AT7 Making new materials
AT17 The nature of science

Syllabus links
   ○ GCSE Science, Chemistry
   ○ A-level Chemistry

Lesson time
    2–3 hours
    (homework possible)

Links with other SATIS materials
207   The Story of Fritz Haber
805   The Search for the Magic Bullet

SATIS 16–19
14   William Perkin

NERIS
Search on
     DYES and UPPER
     SECONDARY

STUDENT ACTIVITIES

☐ Reading and answering questions: how Perkin discovered and manufactured 'mauveine'.

☐ Practical work: making and testing Perkin's mauve. This experiment, as printed on page 5, is no longer considered appropriate for student practical below the sixth-form level.

Please see the information below.

USE

The unit is most suitable for able fifth-form specialist chemistry students or for sixth formers.

ADAPTING THE UNIT

☐ The unit may be used without the experimental work.

☐ Parts A, B and C of the experiment should be demonstrated. (See below.)

☐ The questions may be answered individually or through small group discussion.

☐ The text is presented as a story and is probably best treated as a 'good read'. However, students could be asked to make a glossary of key terms such as, *natural dye, fast (dye), indigo, quinine.*

☐ The Central TV schools' programmes, 'Dyes', deals with the commercial mixing and testing of dyes.

FURTHER INFORMATION

There are safety problems associated with the experimental work in the unit.

There is a risk of the ethanol catching fire. It is suggested that it is warmed with hot water from an electric kettle.

The ASE's publication, *Topics in Safety*, lists dichromates as restricted chemicals. Only sixth formers should handle the solid and phenylammonium salts.

At Key Stage 4, the teacher could either demonstrate the experiment, or do parts A, B and C in the diagrams, before dividing up the precipitate for student use.

First published 1986

Electricity on Demand

Science content

Energy sources for power stations, distribution of electric power on a national scale.

Science curriculum links

AT11 Electricity and magnetism

AT13 Energy

Syllabus links

- GCSE Science, Physics
- Geography
- Sixth-form General Studies

Lesson time

1½ hours

Links with other SATIS materials

701 Electricity in Your Home
704 Electric Lights
1007 240 Volts can Kill
1008 Why 240 Volts?
1010 Can it be done? (questions 12, 13, 34)

SATIS 16–19

25 Why 50 Hz?

BBC Radio SATIS Topics 14–16

Electricity on Demand

NERIS

Search on
ELECTRIC POWER
GENERATION and POWER
STATIONS

STUDENT ACTIVITIES

☐ Reading: the National Grid, types of power station, the North West Region.

☐ Problem-solving task for pairs: to plan the deployment of power stations to meet summer and winter demand curves (cut and stick data supplied).

USE

Suitable for a wide range of abilities. May be used in conjunction with work on the generation and distribution of electrical power. The task needs to be explained clearly to lower ability students.

ADAPTING THE UNIT

☐ Some teachers have used the material as a source of information on the electricity supply industry and omitted the task at the end.

☐ For students familiar with the electricity supply industry, the task may be used alone.

☐ The supporting BBC Radio programme visits the London Control Centre to witness the 'TV pickup' after Neighbours. The programme explains that frequency is high when too much electricity is being generated and falls when demand fails to meet supply. The programme is best used to add reality to the task after reading the introductory text.

☐ Less able students need to have the task explained to them, otherwise they tend to meet the demand with a random selection of power stations.

FURTHER INFORMATION

Since the unit was written some of the power stations in the region have been closed or are scheduled for closure. The nationalised electricity supply industry, the Central Electricity Generating Board (CEGB), has been broken up into four companies.

NEW MATERIAL

The unit has been republished as SATIS 1109, *Electricity Supply and Demand*.

First published 1986

The Limestone Inquiry

Science content

Limestone, uses as a raw material, the effects of exploitation.

Science curriculum links
AT 5   Human influences on the Earth
AT 9   Earth and atmosphere

Syllabus links
○   GCSE Science, Chemistry
○   Geography

Cross-curricular themes
○   Environment
○   Citizenship

Lesson time
1 hour role-play
preparation may be homework

Links with other SATIS materials
502   The Coal Mine Project
1001   Chocolate Chip Mining

BBC Radio SATIS Topics 14–16
The Limestone Inquiry

NERIS
Search on
    LIMESTONE
or
    QUARRYING
Additional search terms
    PHYSICAL PLANNING and
    ROLE PLAY

STUDENT ACTIVITIES

☐ Preparation for role-play: a general briefing about limestone, how it is quarried and its uses.

☐ Role-play public inquiry involving the whole class: the seven interests involved are the: inspectors, the quarrying firm, its customers, the trade unions, the National Parks Authority, local residents and conservationists.

USE

This unit has been successfully used with all abilities in conjunction with carbonate chemistry, industrial chemistry or in geography.

It is popular with both teachers and students. 'The kids loved it.' 'They really got into their roles!'

ADAPTING THE UNIT

☐ The BBC Radio programme helps to set the scene and is best used with the General Briefing.

☐ Some schools have found using a team of three students for the inspectors works better.

☐ Recording the briefings onto tape to be listened to by each group of students can help those of lower ability.

☐ Some classes have produced posters, wall-charts or newspaper articles about the inquiry.

☐ The work may be linked with geography.

UPDATING INFORMATION

☐ Limestone is nowadays converted into quicklime before use in steelmaking. The following amendment is suggested for Figure 3 on student sheet GB2. Delete 'steelmaking' under 'LUMP LIMESTONE'. Add 'steelmaking' under 'QUICKLIME CaO'.

☐ ICI Mond Division no longer exists and is now part of ICI Chemicals and Polymers. The address for correspondence regarding lime products is:
ICI Chemicals and Polymers, PO Box 3, Buxton, Derbyshire SK17 8TH.

☐ *Limestone and Lime Products* is now a Technical Service Booklet, reference TS/E/36. (See Teachers' Notes ii).

First published 1986

The Heart Pacemaker

Science content

Function of the heart, the heart pacemaker–an example of life supporting technology, astable multivibrator.

Science curriculum links
AT3   Processes of life
(AT12 IT including
          microelectronics)

Syllabus links
  ○   GCSE Science, Physics
  ○   Technology

Cross-curricular themes
  ○   Health Education

Lesson time
        1–2 hours
        (homework possible)

Links with other SATIS materials
302   Living with Kidney Failure
506   Materials for Life
707   Artificial Limbs
1010 Can it be done?
        (question 9)

BBC Radio SATIS Topics 14–16
    The Heart Pacemaker

STUDENT ACTIVITIES

☐   Reading and answering questions: the story of a pacemaker patient, how the heart works, causes of heart disease, pacemakers.

☐   Extension practical: building an astable multivibrator (details in the Teachers' Notes).

USE

May be used for revision or extension work on the heart or as an example of an application of electronics.

This unit has been much enjoyed by students and works well over the full ability range. It may also be used for independent study.

ADAPTING THE UNIT

☐   The BBC Radio programme, 'The Heart Pacemaker', complements the latter part of the unit, interviewing a heart surgeon and a technician who programs pacemakers.

☐   Work may be extended to include heart disease and health issues like smoking, diet and exercise.

☐   There are data-logging devices which students can use to log their own pulse rates.

☐   The unit may used as an extension of work in electronics by setting a brief, 'design a device that will send a pulse every second' and then using the SATIS material as an application. The circuit shown in the Teachers' Notes uses standard school components.

UPDATING INFORMATION

☐   'What can go wrong with the heart?' [page 3]. In addition to the reasons given, heart rate abnormalities may have no obvious cause.

☐   'When are pacemakers used?' [page 4]. They may also be used to correct a fast heart rate.

☐   The heart pacemaker is connected to the atrioventricular node, near the 'middle' of the heart. (Impulses controlling a normal heart pass from the sinoatrial node in the right atrium, shown in Figure 4, to both atria and to the atrioventricular node at the junction of the atria and ventricles.)

☐   There are minor omissions from the circuit shown in the Teachers' Notes. An updated diagram is provided.

First published 1986

Components needed for a 9 V d.c. supply:

Transistors: 2 BC 109s

Resistors: 680 Ω, 1 kΩ, 4.7 kΩ, 50 kΩ linear variable.

LED red (or a 6 V lamp may be used instead of the 680 Ω resistor and LED)

Electrolytic capacitors: 100 μF, 470 μF.

Connectors / connecting wire

Oscilloscope (optional)

A simple electronic pulsing circuit:

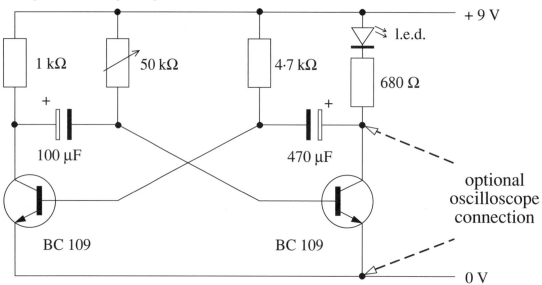

Metals as Resources

Science content

Exploitation of materials (metals) generated by the rock cycle, reactivity series of metals.

Science curriculum links
AT 6   Types and uses of materials
AT 7   Making new materials

Syllabus links
○   GCSE Science, Chemistry,
○   Geography

Cross-curricular themes
○   Economic Awareness

Lesson time
1–2 hours

Links with other SATIS materials
103   Controlling Rust
310   Recycling Aluminium
1001   Chocolate Chip Mining
1010   Can it be done?
        (questions 23 and 29)

STUDENT ACTIVITIES

☐ Reading and answering questions: properties of metals, production and prices.

☐ Drawing conclusions from data: reserves and resources.

☐ Reading and answering more speculative questions: What happens when reserves run out?

USE

To revise and extend work on metal resources. This unit is widely used but is not suitable as it stands for lower ability students.

ADAPTING THE UNIT

☐ The unit may be shortened by using Parts 1 and 2 only.

☐ For lower ability students, shorten the unit and select questions carefully, questions 5 and 12 cause problems for many.

FURTHER INFORMATION

If the new data provided overleaf is used the answer in the Teachers' Notes to Q.1 gives the new order as Fe, Al, Cr, Cu = Mn, Zn.

NEW MATERIAL

New data for Table 1, Table 2 and Figure 4 are provided overleaf. Here are suggestions for incorporating the data.

☐ Make a photocopy and stick the new tables over the old ones on the original masters and reprint the unit.

If you do not wish to reprint the whole unit:

☐ Attach a copy of the page to each unit and ask students to work from the new data.

☐ Cross out the old figures and write in the new ones.

First published 1986

Table 1 World production of metals during the late 1980s. The table lists the nineteen metals produced in the largest quantities, in alphabetical order

Metal	Symbol	World production/thousand tonnes per year
Aluminium	Al	15 500
Antimony	Sb	50
Arsenic	As	40
Chromium	Cr	10 000
Cobalt	Co	30
Copper	Cu	8000
Gold	Au	1.6
Iron	Fe	500 000
Lead	Pb	3500
Magnesium	Mg	300
Manganese	Mn	8000
Molybdenum	Mo	100
Nickel	Ni	800
Silver	Ag	10
Tin	Sn	200
Tungsten	W	40
Uranium	U	35 (Western world total)
Vanadium	V	30
Zinc	Zn	7000

Table 2 Prices and percentage abundance of metals

Metal	Price per tonne (1990)	Abundance % of Earth's crust
Aluminium, Al	£940	8.1
Chromium, Cr	£4,800	0.01
Copper, Cu	£1,600	0.0055
Gold, Au	£7,400,000	0.0000004
Iron, Fe	£130	5.0
Lead, Pb	£530	0.0013
Silver, Ag	£160,000	0.000007
Tin, Sn	£3,900	0.0002
Zinc, Zn	£1,000	0.007

GOLD	25 years
ZINC	25 years
COPPER	40 years
CHROMIUM	100 years
IRON	132 years
ALUMINIUM	240 years

Figure 4 Lifetimes of reserves of some metals

The Great Chunnel Debate

Science content

Environmental impact.

Science curriculum links
AT 5   Human influences on the
        Earth

Syllabus links
- ○ GCSE Science
- ○ Geography
- ○ Sixth-form General Studies
- ○ Technology

Cross-curricular themes
- ○ Environment
- ○ Citizenship
- ○ Economic Awareness

Lesson time
2 hours
(homework possible)

Links with other SATIS materials
501   Bridges
409   Dam Problems
1110 Project Management

NERIS
Search on
    CHANNEL TUNNEL

STUDENT ACTIVITIES

- ☐ Reading and answering questions: the advantages of a fixed link, the plan, costs, the case against the link.

- ☐ Debate: should the Channel Tunnel be built?

USE

As an educational experience to show the complexity of a major engineering project involving science and technology.

This material has also been used in geography, in sixth-form general studies and on teachers' courses.

ADAPTING THE UNIT

- ☐ Students give a mini-lecture for each role, followed by general discussion.

- ☐ The unit may be used by groups of four to six students, with one reporting their decision back to the class.

- ☐ Update the topic by debating: *'Should the Tunnel have been started / built?'*

FURTHER INFORMATION

For the Teachers' Notes:
'The Channel Tunnel Group' is now known as 'Eurotunnel'.

Q6 The advantages of a fixed link

(a) Crossing by Tunnel is independent of the weather. However, the new large ferries are also largely independent of the weather.

(b) Crossing by Tunnel will be faster than ferries. This advantage is decreasing as larger ferries come into service. Dover to Calais times are: ship 135 minutes, hovercraft 80 minutes, Tunnel (estimate) 70 minutes.

(c) No advantage. Driving onto the shuttle has the same disadvantages as driving onto a ship.

(d) Safety considerations, risk of collision or sinking of ferry. (However, there are serious concerns about the risk of train crashes or sabotage causing fire in the Tunnel. Some people question whether fire precautions will be adequate.)

(e) The Tunnel may relieve road congestion (but only if satisfactory rail links are built).

Answers to the remaining questions are updated in the new information.

First published 1986

NEW MATERIAL

A new student page provides updated information and costs.

In view of Eurotunnel's large debt, no figures have been provided for its yearly income and running costs to update Table 1.

It is suggested that students do Part 1 and questions 1 to 7.

Please add to question 7
  'and (c) ferries'

Parts 2 and 3 are now history! However, it is interesting to compare the plans with what has happened. Questions 8 to 11 should be deleted. The 1990 perspective is given in the new material.

It is still possible to have a very vigorous debate on issues concerning the Channel Tunnel.
  'Should the Tunnel have been built?'
  'Should there be a second fixed link?'

OTHER RESOURCES

A wide range of educational publications, including video and slides are available from the Mail Order Department, Eurotunnel Exhibition Centre, St Martin's Plain, Cheriton High Street, Folkestone, Kent CT19 4QD. Tel. 0303 270111. Fax. 0303 270211/2.

Activities

Read Part 1 and answer questions 1 to 7. Add '*and (c) ferries*' to question 7.

Read Parts 2, 3. Omit questions 8 to 11. Read the updating information here. Collect any news items about the Tunnel.

A 1990 perspective

The Great Chunnel Debate was written in 1984–5 while the debate was still raging. 'The Channel Tunnel Group' has taken the name 'Eurotunnel'. Construction began in 1987. The Tunnel is due to open on 15 June, 1993.

The construction of the privately-financed Tunnel has been eventful. Tunnel construction costs were underestimated.

Eurotunnel called an Extraordinary General Meeting on 20 June 1990 to increase its share capital. They put their costs as

Construction costs	£4933 million
Owning group costs	£ 718 million
Provision for inflation	£ 329 million
Borrowing	£1686 million
Total cash required (*to the date of opening*)	£7666 million

It is interesting to compare these costs with those predicted in Table 1 in the unit and notice the how large the cost of borrowing money to finance the project has been. The figures put to shareholders may well be 'truthful' but conceal more interest charges bringing the bill up to £8300 million.

At the same time, Eurotunnel announced that they will take until 2042 to repay the debt (that is, 55 years from the start of the graph in Figure 5). This happens to be the year in which its concession agreement for operating the Tunnel will run out. Of course, the government may decide to renew its concession or it may give it to a different company.

Eurotunnel must create some income with which to pay its shareholders, but the figures in Table 1 are no longer realistic. Critics suspect that the figures put to the shareholders in June 1990 may have to rise again before all the work is finished.

A second fixed link

The government retains the option after 2010 to offer a franchise for a second fixed link. This is intended to be a road tunnel and is to be constructed by the year 2020. A drive-through tunnel or bridge will not require the construction of expensive terminals at each end. Eurotunnel will have to expect some loss of revenue to the new competition.

Competition from the ferries

While interest in the 1980s centred on a fixed link, the prospects of improvement in the ferry services were largely overlooked.

The new large ferries are fast. They can maintain a regular service even during severe weather – an advantage that the Tunnel was supposed to have. If the ferry companies provide a half-hourly no-reservation service, it is likely to be extremely competitive with the Tunnel. Driving onto a ship is no less convenient than driving onto a shuttle for the Tunnel.

There needs to be massive investment in new road and particularly rail links to the Tunnel or its potential may not be realised. Proposals for the Channel Tunnel included new high-speed trains running on special track. This rail link seems unlikely to be built.

Critics wonder whether with increased costs Eurotunnel will be able to offer fares that are competitive with those of the ferries and still make a profit.

Safety considerations

Although there are worries about the safety of car ferries, the safety record of Cross-Channel ferries is good (in spite of the sinking of the *Herald of Free Enterprise* at Zeebrugge).

There are concerns too about safety in the Tunnel. What if trains crash or are sabotaged? While Eurotunnel seek to reassure, critics say that not enough money is being spent on safety.

There are other worries too. Will people like travelling through the Tunnel? Or will some suffer claustrophobia? Will a fixed link aid the spread of rabies to the UK?

Tristan da Cunha Dental Surveys

Science content

Diet and dental decay.

Science curriculum links
AT 1 Exploration of science
AT 3 Processes of life

Syllabus links
○ GCSE Science, Biology

Cross-curricular themes
○ Health Education

Lesson time
1 hour

Links with other SATIS materials
401 Fluoridation of Water
       Supplies
1010 Can it be done?
       (question 24)
1104 Materials to Repair Teeth

NERIS
Search on
       TOOTH DECAY and DIET

STUDENT ACTIVITIES

Reading, drawing conclusions from data and answering questions: data relating diet to dental health.

USE

In association with work on diet and health.

This unit is popular with pupils of average ability and above.

Teachers like it because it is short and contains 'real data'. Teachers may need to intervene if weaker students need help with the vocabulary. The unit has also been used with second and third years.

ADAPTING THE UNIT

☐ Weak readers need some help in picturing the way of life on Tritan da Cunha and in understanding why the data from this long isolated community is so useful. They may also need help with vocabulary, such as *inhabitants, communications, refined food, fixed genetic pattern, changes in the environment (in this case meaning diet)*.

☐ The dates of the surveys are not equally spaced. Some students may need to be warned of this before plotting the graph.

NEW MATERIAL

There is a new page 3 with an alternative set of questions to make the unit more accessible.

First published 1986

Tristan da Cunha (pronounced Cue-na), is a small island formed by a volcano.

In the twentieth century, ships sometimes called to sell the islanders foods and other items which they did not produce for themselves.

Weak enamel on teeth and patterns of tooth decay may run in families. Drinking water can affect tooth decay (as you will see if you use the SATIS unit, *Fluoridation of Water Supplies*). It is difficult for scientists to collect data on patterns of tooth decay because many families in Britain move from place to place.

Q1 *Describe where it is.*

Q2 *How did people come to live on the island and stay there?*

Q3 *How many people lived there in 1880?*

Q4 *What did they have to eat?*

Q5 *Look at Table 1. How had the diet of the people on Tristan da Cunha changed between 1880 and 1937?*

Q6 *What happened to their teeth?*

Q7 *Suggest how the islanders earned money to pay for goods the ships brought them (a) before 1949, (b) after 1949.*

Q8 *How had the diet of the islanders changed by the time of the surveys in the 1950s?*

Q9 *Why are the figures from Tristan da Cunha so interesting?*

Q10 *What do the following terms in the unit mean? (a) inhabitants, (b) refined food, (b) fixed genetic pattern?*

Use the information in Table 1 to draw a graph. Show the percentage of people with good teeth, that is, **free from tooth decay**, against the **date** of the survey.

- Make the date axis horizontal. Number the scale from 1930 to 1960.

- Make the scale on the percentage axis run from 0 to 100.

- To start plotting, find **1932** on the **date axis**. Then find where this date crosses the value of 83.3% (you can call it 83%) and plot the point.

- Plot points for all the dates. Draw as smooth a curve as you can through the four points.

Q11 *Describe in words what your graph shows. What do the results of the survey suggest?*

Q12 *Suggest why there was no survey between 1937 and 1952.*

Q13 *Write a few sentences explaining the causes of dental decay.*

In 1961 the volcano erupted. The islanders were rescued by the Royal Navy and brought to Britain. Many islanders were unhappy. When the volcano on their island was safe they returned.

Scale and Scum

Science content

Hard water, soft water, lather, energy, health.

Science curriculum links
AT 5 Human influences on the Earth
AT 7 Making new materials

Syllabus links
○ GCSE Science, Chemistry
○ Sixth-form General Studies

Cross-curricular themes
○ Citizenship

Lesson time
1 hour

Links with other SATIS materials
401 Fluoridation of Water Supplies
709 Which Anti-acid?
801 The Water Pollution Mystery

BBC Radio SATIS Topics 14–16
Scale and Scum

NERIS
Search on
HARD WATER

STUDENT ACTIVITIES

☐ Looking at advertising claims and answering questions: hard water, scale in the hot tank, soap lather, drinking water etc.

☐ Discussion.

USE

With work on water or carbon dioxide chemistry to foster a scientific attitude towards advertisers' claims.

Suitable for all abilities and regarded by some teachers as an ideal SATIS unit.

'... my unmotivated group got quite interested.' 'Holiday work. Great fun!'

ADAPTING THE UNIT

☐ Page 2 can be used as the basis of a role-play done in pairs, the customer – the doorstep water softener salesman.

☐ 'One pair wrote a song and sang it!'

☐ The large amount of photocopying has been a problem for some schools. Suggestions made by teachers are – photo-reducing pages 3 to 9 to half size and printing two per page;

– keeping these pages separate and having students share them;

– sealing the the pages in film to pass around the class.

☐ The BBC Radio programme supporting this unit does not deal with water softeners but focuses on the validity of advertising claims. It considers claims for an imaginary food product, Skinnybix, a slimming biscuit. This programme may also be used with work on diet.

First published 1986

Should we Build a Fallout Shelter?

Science content

Radioactive emissions, their effect on matter and living organisms, necessities for human survival.

Science curriculum links
AT 3 Processes of life
AT 8 Explaining how materials behave

Syllabus links
○ GCSE Science, Physics
○ Sixth-form General Studies

Cross-curricular themes
○ Health Education
○ Citizenship

Lesson time
1 hour

Links with other SATIS materials
109 Nuclear Power
204 Using Radioactivity
404 How Would You Survive?
807 Radiation
808 Nuclear Fusion
1105 Radon

STUDENT ACTIVITIES

☐ Preparation for role-play: general briefing – saving lives in the event of nuclear war.

☐ Role-play inquiry (or debate) involving the whole class: five roles, the remainder of the class forming the audience.

☐ Coming out of role, follow-up discussion (not suggested in the unit itself).

USE

With work on radioactivity. For some students it provides a welcome relief from a very abstract part of the curriculum.

It might be pointed out to students that all homes in Switzerland have fallout shelters and that these shelters are kept stocked with emergency rations.

Students need to be carefully chosen to take on the roles (best done in pairs – but see the Teachers' Notes). The discussion may become quite emotional and students should be allowed to come out of role and put their personal point of view in a follow-up discussion.

ADAPTING THE UNIT

☐ The unit may be run as a debate rather than an inquiry. Students do better in the more formal and combative atmosphere.

☐ Students taking on the main roles would benefit from having time to prepare their roles in advance at home.

☐ The remaining students could produce an 'information leaflet for householders' explaining radioactivity, half-life and shielding (how alpha, beta and gamma radiation can be absorbed – as in SATIS 204).

First published 1986

Hitting the Target

Science content

Enhancement of the body's natural defences against disease, an example of a scientific advance.

Science curriculum links
AT3 Processes of life
AT17 The nature of science

Syllabus links
○ GCSE Science, Biology
○ A-level Biology

Cross-curricular themes
○ Health Education

Lesson time
1–2 hours

STUDENT ACTIVITIES

☐ Reading and answering questions: the antibody-antigen interaction, monoclonal antibodies, work awarded Nobel prizes.

☐ Solving problems with monoclonal antibodies: detecting pregnancy, treating leukaemia, treating haemophilia, finding cancers.

USE

This unit is more suitable for able students. It may be used as an extension to work on the body's defences against disease and to learn about an important aspect of biotechnology. The unit portrays the process of scientific discovery.

Alternative material is provided to make it accessible to a much wider range of students.

ADAPTING THE UNIT

☐ Use parts or all of the extension material.

UPDATING INFORMATION

The sentence on page 4, first paragraph, 'Tumours inside the body can be a serious problem and some tumours cause cancer' would be more accurate if it said 'Tumours inside the body can be a serious problem particularly if they spread to other sites.'

NEW MATERIAL

Re-presented content

☐ Strip cartoon explaining what monoclonal antibodies do.

☐ Simple summary of page 6.

Activities which may be used with the original unit or with the new pages

☐ Diagrams to cut and stick.

☐ Missing word exercise.

☐ Questions.

First published 1986

Q1   *Cut out the antibody and antigen diagrams. Stick them*
together to make more of the antibody-antigen complex.

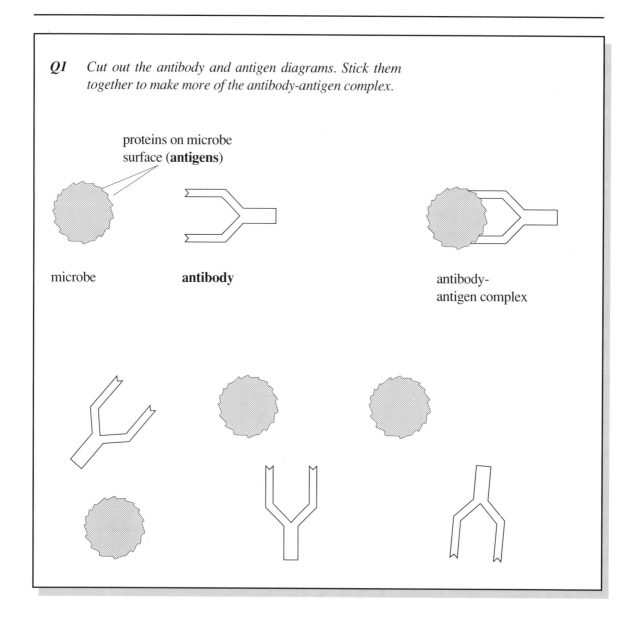

> **Q2** Copy the following. Fill in the spaces with the words from the list. Use each word once only.
>
> ANTIBODIES, ANTIGENS, ATTACH, ATTACHED, LYMPHOCYTES, MONOCLONAL, PHAGOCYTES, PROTEINS.
>
> - _____ attack viruses. They are made by the _____ .
> - All viruses and bacteria have special shaped _____ on their surface which are called _____ .
> - This special pattern helps the antibody find and _____ itself to the antigen on the virus it wants to kill.
> - After the antigen has done its job and the virus is dead, the rubbish collecting cells, called _____ get rid of them.
> - Antibodies which are all the same type are called _____ antibodies.
> - If a strong drug needs to be used in the body to treat a disease like cancer, it can be _____ to the monoclonal antibodies. That way only the bad part is attacked.

Using monoclonal antibodies

Kits can be made to find diseases in the body. The kits contain **monoclonal antibodies**. The antibodies are made to fit the **antigens** on the disease microbes.

When a solution of the antibodies is added to the ill person's blood or urine it can be made to change colour. You then know that the ill person has the disease.

Monoclonal antibodies are not only used to find diseases. They can be used to find out if a woman is pregnant. If she is pregnant, her urine contains certain chemicals.

> **Q3** If you have had an illness once, you can't catch it again. Why?
>
> **Q4** Why do you think you can catch 'flu more than once?
>
> **Q5** Antibodies which fight measles do not work against chicken pox. Why?
>
> **Q6** What is the name of a killer disease that could be treated with a drug attached to monoclonal antibodies?
>
> **Q7** How are monoclonal antibodies used to find out if a woman is pregnant?

Robots at Work

Science content

Control by feedback, sensors.

Science curriculum links
AT12 IT including
microelectronics

Syllabus links
- GCSE Science, Physics,
- Sixth-form General Studies
- Technology

Cross-curricular themes
- Careers
- Economic Awareness

Lesson time
1½ hours
(homework possible)

Links with other SATIS materials
507   Computers and Jobs
905   The impact of IT
906   IT in Greenhouses

NERIS
Search on
INDUSTRIAL ROBOTS

STUDENT ACTIVITIES

☐ Reading: industrial robots, feedback control, sensors, control centre, actuators, robots and human jobs.

☐ Decision-making activity for pairs: a robot for spraying – is it worth buying?

☐ Questions for answer or discussion.

USE

To follow-up work on control technology and to highlight its social and economic implications.

The unit has been found to be suitable for more able and well-motivated students. The organisational skills for the decision-making activity are at quite a high level.

ADAPTING THE UNIT

☐ Less able students may be helped by text-related activities such as the questions provided here.

FURTHER INFORMATION

The decision to buy a robot should be based on whether it will be cost effective. The robot should save human effort or increase sales or both.

If society's needs were static, engineering innovations would continually erode jobs. Society at large continually acquires new appetites for satisfaction. Human skills are used in creating new products to satisfy the changes in society.

NEW MATERIAL

Questions linked to pages 1 to 4 are printed so that questions 1, 2 and 3 may be photocopied and fitted into the narrow column of page 2. Question 4 belongs with page 3.

First published 1986

Questions linked to pages 1 to 4

---

1   *What is an industrial robot?*

2   *What are the robots used for in*
        (a) Figure 2,
        (b) Figure 5,
        (c) Figure 7,
        (d) Figure 8?

3   *In how many directions can the robot in Figure 4 swivel?*
        Why are so many directions needed?

---

4   *What sort of sensor is providing feedback information to the robot in*
        (a) Figure 5,
        (b) Figure 2,
        (c) Figure 8?

Electricity in your Home

Science content

Measurement and cost of domestic electrical energy use by electric meter readings.

Science curriculum links
AT11 Electricity and magnetism

Syllabus links
○ GCSE Science, Physics,

Cross-curricular themes
○ Economic Awareness

Lesson time
1–2 hours
(plus homeworks)

Links with other SATIS materials
403   Britain's Energy Sources
704   Electric Lights
1109 Electricity Supply and Demand

NERIS
Search on
        ELECTRICITY SUPPLY
        METERS
Additional search term
        ELECTRICITY USE

STUDENT ACTIVITIES

☐ Reading: kilowatt-hour, electricity meters.

☐ Data gathering, drawing a bar chart: measuring the use of electricity in the home over several days.

☐ Electricity use by different appliances: measurements to make at home.

USE

As part of work on domestic energy. Enjoyed by well-motivated groups of all abilities.

Students have found the activities, which need a certain degree of perseverance, extremely rewarding and an educational experience for the whole family. However, parental co-operation is needed. There may be difficulties in encroachment on sensitive family matters. Some teachers have found that students refuse to carry out the activities at home, or parents refuse to allow them.

Schools with a mounted meter have been able to do Part 2 in class.

ADAPTING THE UNIT

☐ Have some data handy for students who do not carry out the home activities.

☐ Some students need considerable help in reading meter dials before they start. The local electricity board has free leaflets on how to read a meter.

FURTHER INFORMATION

New meters are solid state with a digital readout. A pulsing red light has replaced the disc. A diagram is provided overleaf.

Remote reading of meters is technically possible and may eventually be introduced.

OTHER RESOURCES

The software package *A Town like Wattville* provides simulations relevant to this unit. Details are available from Understanding Electricity, The Electricity Association, 30 Millbank, London SW1P 4RD.

NEW MATERIAL

Diagram of a digital domestic meter.

First published 1986

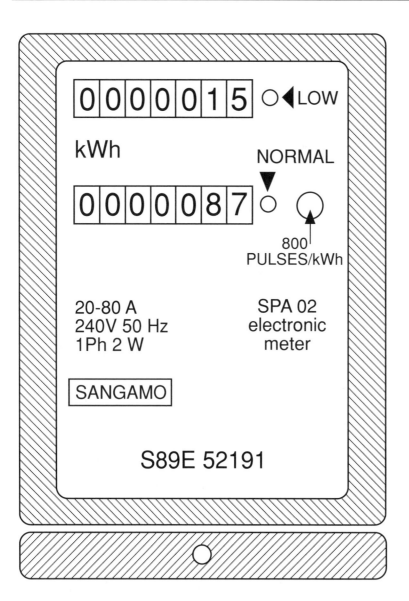

Solid State Meter

The Gas Supply Problem

Science content

Energy from methane, storage and transfer of gas, end use.

Science curriculum links
AT13 Energy

Syllabus links
○ GCSE Science, Chemistry, Physics,

Lesson time
1½ **hours**
(homework possible)

Links with other SATIS materials
403 Britain's Energy Sources
601 Electricity on Demand
908 Why not Combined Heat and Power?

NERIS
Search on
UPPER SECONDARY and GAS SUPPLY
or on
UPPER SECONDARY and NATURAL GAS
additional search term
GAS PIPELINES

STUDENT ACTIVITIES

☐ Reading: information about natural gas, its uses, its distribution.

☐ Problem-solving: designing a gas distribution system.

USE

As extension work on sources of energy. (The information parallels electricity supply and the National Grid.)

The material is considered rather difficult for lower abilities.

Page 6 should be held back until the end of the lesson!

ADAPTING THE UNIT

☐ Questions linking with the text to prime students for the problem-solving task are given in the new material.

☐ The Teachers' Notes contain a lot of useful data which could form the basis of data interpretation exercises.

FURTHER INFORMATION

The unit gives gas pressures in atmospheres. The equivalent values in bar are:
Long distance gas mains (over 70 atmospheres) 70 bar
Factories (medium pressure) 1 bar
Homes (low pressure) 75 mbar
(1 atmosphere is approximately 1 bar, the pressure in car tyres is approximately 2 bar.)

British Gas now supply seventeen million customers and have 248 000 km of gas mains. (A small increase over the figures in the unit.)

OTHER RESOURCES

British Gas produce a laboratory gas meter with a digital display for educational use. Details of this and other educational items, including software, are available from British Gas Education Service, PO Box 46, Hounslow, Middlesex TW4 6NF.

NEW MATERIAL

Questions and graph plotting related to the text.

First published 1986

Questions about pages 1 to 3

Q1   Why does natural gas have a smell?

Q2   The main sources of energy available for heating and cooking in the UK are coal, oil, electricity and gas. Many homes use gas. Suggest why this is.

Q3   Redraw the pie charts on page 2 (Figure 2, Figure 3 and Figure 4) as bar charts.

Q4   What are gas pipes made from?

Q5   What could cause gas pipes to leak?

Q6   Why do steel gas pipes need protecting from corrosion?

Nowadays, steel pipes are protected from rusting by waterproof wrapping and by cathodic protection. Either an electric current is sent along the pipe or sacrificial anodes are fixed to the pipe. (There's more about this in SATIS 103, *Controlling Rust*.)

Q7   Why it is important to detect leaks?

Q8   What makes the intelligent pig move along the gas pipe?

Questions about page 4

Q9   What is the pressure in long distance gas mains?

Q10 Why are long distance gas mains much wider than local gas mains?

Q11 Arrange these in the order of the gas pressure used inside them: local mains to factories, mains to houses, long-distance mains.

Q12 Suggest how the gas industry copes with the demand for gas varying during the day.

Q13 What is the purpose of compressor stations on the gas mains?

Q14 How many compressor stations are needed for a main 100 km long?

Hint. When you tackle the problem, you will need to put in pressure reduction stations between high pressure gas mains and lower pressure ones.

Vegetarianism

Science content

Diet, digestive system, agriculture, ecosystem management.

Science curriculum links
AT 2   The variety of life
AT 3   Processes of life

Syllabus links
○   GCSE Science, Biology
○   Sixth-form General Studies

Cross-curricular themes
○   Health Education
○   Environment
○   Economic Awareness

Lesson time
    1–2 hours

Links with other SATIS materials
102   Food from Fungus
108   Fibre in you Diet
208   The Price of Food
1010 Can it be done?
      (questions 7, 27, 30)

SATIS 16–19
5   Animal rights and animals
      wrongs

NERIS
Search on
      VEGETARIANISM
Additional search term
      ANIMAL RIGHTS

STUDENT ACTIVITIES

☐   Reading, data interpretation and answering questions: types of vegetarian, the arguments about cruelty, health, energy and economics.

☐   Discussion points.

USE

Links with work on digestion, nutrition, also with energy transfer along food chains.

Suitable for all abilities.
    'Working in small groups – that got them really going!!'
    ' ... led to a debate, boys just as involved as girls.'

ADAPTING THE UNIT

☐   Organise a debate with a provocative title (such as 'The Government should ban the eating of meat.')

☐   Produce an argument against vegetarianism from the viewpoint of the cattle or sheep farmer.

☐   Use new discussion points.

FURTHER INFORMATION

Although arable farming is the most efficient way of producing food, sheep, goats and deer are able to use land which is unsuitable for most crops. There is growing interest in the return to sustainable mixed farming practices with animal manure or composted plant material returning fertility to the soil.

Further points for discussion

☐   What do pet dogs and cats eat? Where does it come from? Should vegetarians keep pet cats and dogs?

☐   Organic farming uses no artificial fertilizers or insecticides. Instead the soil is usually fertilized with manure from animals (although it is possible to use compost from decaying plant matter). These animals are normally reared for food and eventually slaughtered. Do you think vegetarians should eat food grown in this way?

☐   The Inuit in the far north of Canada (see SATIS 404 *How Would You Survive?*) survive by hunting wild animals. The Lapps (Saami) live in arctic Europe. They survive by keeping herds of reindeer. Growing crops is impossible.

–   *Do you think it is immoral for the Inuit to hunt their food?*
–   *Is herding animals, like the Lapps, better?*
–   *Should these peoples be persuaded to abandon their traditional way of life and become vegetarians?*

First published 1986

Electric Lights

Science content

Electrical energy, efficiency, resistance, filament lamps, gas discharge lamps, fluorescent lamps.

Science curriculum links
AT11 Electricity and magnetism
AT13 Energy
AT15 Using light and electromagnetic radiation

Syllabus links
○ GCSE Science, Physics

Cross-curricular themes
○ Economic Awareness

Lesson time
1 hour
(and homework)

Links with other SATIS materials
701 Electricity in Your Home
1007 Why 240 Volts?
1109 Electricity Supply and Demand

NERIS
Search on
ELECTRIC LAMPS

STUDENT ACTIVITIES

☐ Homework survey: electric lights in the home.

☐ Reading and answering questions: information about different types of electric lights. Comparing the costs of using filament and fluorescent lights.

USE

As extension work on the use of electricity or energy in the home.

A fairly difficult unit, better suited to able students. The home survey will need parental co-operation.

ADAPTING THE UNIT

☐ Questions need to be selected carefully for less able students.

☐ Alternatively, confine the work to domestic lamps only.

☐ To make the home survey simple, students could examine different types of light bulb in the classroom and then complete the home survey table.

☐ Measure the energy used by a compact fluorescent lamp and a filament lamp. See the experiment in SATIS 701, *Electricity in Your Home*, Part 2.

FURTHER INFORMATION

☐ The information in the unit is increasingly topical with concerns about the burning of fossil fuels and the contribution that it makes to the Greenhouse Effect. Compact fluorescent lamps are now widely available (life about 5000 hours, cost around £9). They not only save energy, but as they last four times longer, save on labour costs of regularly replacing bulbs. They are best used where lamps are left on for long periods of time. One US Utility Company is giving them away to avoid having to build an additional power station.

☐ For Table 3 on page 5, the cost of a compact tube is now about £2.70 and a light bulb about 40p.

☐ Tungsten halogen lamps are now sold for domestic use as compact lamps, especially where it is safer to use low voltage lamps – for desk lamps, spot lamps and bedhead lamps. They usually work on a 12V supply and need a mains transformer. In desk lamps it is often incorporated in the design of the base. There are concerns about the amount of ultraviolet light they emit. It is advisable not to look straight at them or to use them as reading lamps for long periods of time.

First published 1986

Physics in Playgrounds

Science content

Force, weight, friction, acceleration, gpe, ke, velocity, frequency, oscillation, [circular motion].

Science curriculum links
AT10 Forces
AT13 Energy
AT14 Sound and music

Syllabus links
○ GCSE Science, Physics

Cross-curricular links
○ Citizenship

Lesson time
1–2 hours

Links with other SATIS units
504 How Safe is Your Car?
809 Ball Games

SATIS 16–19
47 Playing safe

STUDENT ACTIVITIES

☐ Reading and questions:
  - Playing in a giant's laboratory: recall of childhood experiences; public responsibility for playgrounds.
  - Slides: energy, force, motion, friction, acceleration.
  - Swings: oscillation, frequency, time, energy transfer, gravitational potential energy and kinetic energy.
  - See-saws: weight and weightlessness.
  - Roundabouts: circular motion. Additional material.

USE

For revision of concepts. Suitable for more able students who should be familiar with key words and concepts before they attempt it. Good for developing understanding of energy transfer between gravitational potential energy and kinetic energy. Harder questions are towards the end of each part and could be omitted. May be used for homework.

ADAPTING THE UNIT

Each part may be used separately.

NEW MATERIAL

Roundabouts (circular motion)
Answers to the new student questions on roundabouts

R1 On the roundabout you have another frame of reference and see the world spinning about it.

R2 Yes, going round and round feels different.

R3 The roundabout exerts a pull towards the centre (a centripetal force).

R4 The force gets greater.

R5 (a) At the centre, you will land at the centre. (b) At the edge, you will land off the roundabout. If you say that the roundabout will move around underneath you and you will land at another place, you are almost right. Actually, even though you jump straight up, you will start off with the sideways velocity you had on the roundabout.

R6 The energy you transfer becomes rotational kinetic energy of the roundabout.

R7 A fast moving roundabout stores a lot of energy because it has a lot of mass distributed far from the axis. In effect, it's a flywheel, which is a device used for storing energy. To stop it, you must dissipate this energy – as heat to the mechanism, the stoppers' hands, shoe soles etc.

R8 Young children are surprised by centripetal force.

First published 1986

Roundabouts

Can you remember the first time you rode on a roundabout? The strange force you experienced may have surprised you.

R1   *If you watch somebody riding on a roundabout you see them going round and round about the axis of the roundabout. What impression of the world do you get if you are riding on the roundabout?*

R2   *Does going round and round feel different from going in a straight line – like down a slide?*

R3   *You have to hold on tight. In what direction does the roundabout pull on you?*

R4   *What happens to the force the roundabout exerts on you if the roundabout goes faster and faster?*

R5   *Imagine you tried to jump straight up while the roundabout was going around. What would happen to you if you were (a) at the centre of the roundabout, (b) on the edge?*

R6   *Starting a playground roundabout spinning is hard work. What happens to the energy you transfer to it?*

R7   *Why are fast spinning roundabouts so hard to stop?*

R8   *Large heavy roundabouts have been removed from children's playgrounds because children had accidents on them. Try to explain the causes of the accidents.*

Dry Cells

Science content

Electrochemical cells, electrodes, electrolyte, tests for anions and cations.

Science curriculum links
AT1   Exploration of science
AT13 Energy

Syllabus links
○ GCSE Science, Chemistry, Physics
○ A-level Physics/Chemistry

Lesson time
2 hours
(and homework)

Links with other SATIS materials
202   Electric Vehicles

NERIS
Search on
BATTERIES

STUDENT ACTIVITIES

☐ Survey of home and shops for different types of cell.

☐ Reading and answering questions on cells: simple, zinc-carbon, alkaline manganese, button, nickel-cadmium.

☐ Practical investigations: the chemicals in dry cells (other investigations are suggested below).

USE

As extension work on electrochemistry.

This unit contains interesting information, which is not easily found elsewhere, about an everyday product. Part 1 is suitable for average students, but the following work is quite challenging and more suitable for able students.

The Teachers' Notes contain more information on dry cells.

Opening dry cells for practical work should be done by a technician. Cells may be clamped in a vice and sawn with a hacksaw. *Students should be aware that other types of cell must not be opened.*

In the experimental work on page 7 (a) (i), students should use a loose-fitting cork or bung rather than their thumbs to trap the gas evolved.

ADAPTING THE UNIT

☐ Less able students could do Part 1 and follow it up by one of the investigations suggested here.

☐ Compare the e.m.f.s of a variety of cells with a voltmeter.

☐ How long does it take to flatten a cell? Use a cell in a circuitboard, an ammeter and one, two, three or four lamps in parallel or in series. The investigation can be extended into finding the 'resting time' for the cells to recover. (The cells cease to work if discharged fairly quickly because of a build up of hydrogen bubbles. The oxidising agent converts it into water.)

☐ Investigate the recharge and discharge time of a rechargeable cell.

FURTHER INFORMATION

1990 prices of cells for Teachers' Notes ii.

zinc-carbon, ordinary quality	£0.45
zinc-carbon, top quality	£0.70
alkaline manganese	£1.15
nickel-cadmium rechargeable	£3.50

First published 1986

Artificial Limbs

Science content

Support and movement, nerves, muscles, forces, uses of materials.

Science curriculum links
AT 3   Processes of life

Syllabus links
○   GCSE Science, Biology
○   Human Biology
○   Technology

Cross-curricular themes
○   Health Education

Lesson time
1–2 hours
(homework possible)

Links with other SATIS materials
209   Spectacles and Contact Lenses
506   Materials for Life
603   The Heart Pacemaker

STUDENT ACTIVITIES

☐   Reading and answering questions: introduction, case studies, how artificial limbs work.

☐   Discussion points: the personal issues.

USE

Links with work on the skeleton, nervous system and materials. Suitable for all abilities. For independent work with small group discussion use as a follow-up.

The information provides useful starting points for design work in technology.

ADAPTING THE UNIT

☐   Produce a glossary of terms such as: *arteriosclerosis, gangrene, amputate, physiotherapy, manipulate, electrical impulses, contract, amplified.*

☐   Make model artificial limbs with construction kits.

FURTHER INFORMATION

☐   Helen completed her degree course, subsequently did an MSc course and is now studying for her PhD.

☐   The supply of artificial limbs by the Disablement Services Authority is due to be amalgamated into the NHS in April 1991. There are 30 limbfitting centres around the country. It may be possible to arrange a visit or a visiting speaker by contacting a local centre.

☐   *More about gangrene (for page 1)* Gas gangrene, an *infection* is extremely rare. However, if the blood supply to the legs becomes severely reduced then a *condition* called gangrene may develop. Gangrene usually starts in the toes and works up the leg. A gangrenous foot looks discoloured or even black due to the death of muscle and skin. The leg may have to be amputated to stop the gangrene spreading.

First published 1986

Appropriate Pumps

Science content

Water management, turning forces, explanations of effects of forces.

Science curriculum links

AT5 Human Influences on the Earth

AT10 Forces

Syllabus links
- GCSE Science, Physics
- Geography
- Technology

Cross-curricular themes
- Health Education

Lesson time
   1–2 hours
   (homework possible)

Links with other SATIS materials

404   How Would You Survive?
803   The Technology of Toilets

NERIS
Search on
        WATER SUPPLY and
        DEVELOPING AREAS

STUDENT ACTIVITIES

☐ Reading and questions: why pumps are needed, types of pump, appropriate technology.

☐ Discussion questions.

USE

As an extension to work on forces and mechanisms. Suitable for average and above average students. Some find the diagrams difficult to interpret.

This unit needs sensitive use with students from developing countries. It should not be taken to infer that only developing countries use simple technology.

The unit could provide starting points for modelling pumps and for design opportunities for technological activity.

ADAPTING THE UNIT

☐ Get students to make a device for raising water.

☐ Add some calculations, for example, the work done in raising a bucket of water 10 metres.

☐ Look for evidence of old pumps, wells, Archimedean screws etc. in the locality.

First published 1986

Which Anti-acid?

Science content

Acids, alkalis, carbonates, neutalization.

Science curriculum links
AT 1 Exploration of science
AT 7 Making new materials

Syllabus links
○ GCSE Science, Chemistry
○ A-level Chemistry

Cross-curricular themes
○ Health Education
○ Economic Awareness

Lesson time
1 hour or more

Links with other SATIS materials
904 Which Bleach?
1103 Save the Salmon!

STUDENT ACTIVITIES

☐ Practical data gathering and evaluation: the ingredients in anti-acids.

☐ Answering questions: economic implications of marketing and manufacturing.

☐ Practical investigation: titration to compare the amounts of active ingredient in indigestion remedies.

USE

To extend work on acids, alkalis and carbonates.

This material has been adapted and used with ages ranging from third form to A-level.

It is suggested that teachers have extra tablets available for the titration in Part 3, so that packets used in Part 1 are not damaged.

ADAPTING THE UNIT

☐ Some teachers simplify Table 1 into the chemical aspects (A to D) and costs (E to H).

☐ Add a little water to the crushed tablets (page 4, stage B) before titration, it works much better.

☐ In the titration, aluminium oxide drifts rather slowly to an end point. An alternative is to use a back titration. Drop the tablet into a measured quantity of 0.1 M HCl (aq) in a beaker and stir with a glass rod to dissolve. This models the stomach with acid in it. Portions of the solution are then titrated to find out how much acid was left in the 'stomach'.

The back titration has been used for revising work on moles. For the calculations, students have used a table with the following headings:

Name of tablet

Name of active ingredient

Formula

Molar Mass

Mass of active ingredient in 1 tablet

Number of moles of active ingredient

Number of moles of HCl which can be neutralised by active ingredient in 1 tablet

Total number of moles of HCl neutralised by 1 tablet

First published 1986

What is Biotechnology?

Science content

Fermentation, microbes, enzymes, antibiotics, penicillin, genetic engineering, single cell protein, copper mining, interferon.

Science curriculum links

AT3   Processes of life
AT4   Genetics and evolution
AT7   Making new materials
AT17   The nature of science

Syllabus links

○   GCSE Science, Biology
○   Sixth-form General Studies

Cross-curricular themes

○   Health Education
○   Economic Awareness

Lesson time

1–2 hours
(depending on case studies used)

Links with other SATIS materials

102   Food from Fungus
201   Energy from Biomass
309   Microbes make Human Insulin
609   Hitting the Target
1010   Can it be done?
       (questions 23, 29)
1202   Mapping the Human Genome

SATIS 16–19

57   Pregnancy testing

NERIS

Search on
       BIOTECHNOLOGY and
       UPPER SECONDARY

Additional search terms
       GENETIC ENGINEERING
       INTERFERON
       ENZYMES

STUDENT ACTIVITIES

☐ Reading and answering questions: the development of biotechnology.

☐ Case studies (please refer to the further information below): Case 1 Food from bacteria; Case 2 Using bacteria to extract metals from ores; Case 3 Making interferon; Case 4 Genes in the washing machine.

USE

As example of scientific advances, the discovery of enzymes, penicillin and the use of genetic engineering. This unit provides a general introduction to biotechnology.

Case study 1, is no longer current.

ADAPTING THE UNIT

☐ The unit may be used in parts.

FURTHER INFORMATION

☐ *Case study 1* Pruteen is no longer made. The process was uneconomic compared with alternative sources of animal feed. The large fermenter shown on page 5 is being dismantled to be replaced by several smaller fermenters. These should give greater production flexibility, allowing a variety of products to be made by fermentation.

☐ *Case study 2* This remains an excellent example of an application of biotechnology.

☐ *Case study 3* Once people had enough interferon for clinical trials, it was found *not* to be the promised wonder drug. Interferon was not particularly successful for treating colds; in fact, one notable side-effect of its use was a variety of 'flu-like' symptoms!

OTHER RESOURCES

The National Centre for Biotechnology Education, Department of Microbiology, University of Reading gives advice and publishes a newsletter.

NEW MATERIAL

The unit has been republished as SATIS 1204, *From Babylon to Biotechnology*.

First published 1986

The Water Pollution Mystery

Science content

Water supply, water purity, pH and oxygen content, pollutants.

Science curriculum links
AT 1 Exploration of science
AT 5 Human Influences on the Earth

Syllabus links
 ○ GCSE Science, Biology, Chemistry

Cross-curricular themes
 ○ Environment

Lesson time
 2 hours
 (homework possible)

Links with other SATIS materials
110 Hilltop – an agricultural problem
301 Air Pollution
1103 Save the Salmon!

BBC Radio SATIS Topics 14–16
 The Water Pollution Mystery

NERIS
Search on
 WATER POLLUTION and
 DECISION MAKING or
 INVESTIGATIONS
or on
 WATER POLLUTION
 and UPPER SECONDARY

STUDENT ACTIVITIES

☐ Data interpretation, reading and answering questions (individual or group work): possible evidence for fish deaths. (There is no conclusive evidence.)

☐ Reading, writing a newspaper article: explaining a new theory, fish had the 'bends'.

USE

Following work on water management and pollution – very suitable for balanced science courses. Used from third year to sixth form and over all abilities. Students will need to be able to recall that gases are soluble in water.

This unit is very popular because it is concerned with solving a real environmental problem. Lower ability students need support to succeed.

Do not give out Part 2 until students have tried to find a solution to Part 1. There is no obvious solution. Some students are disappointed, but this is a real example. Part 2 presents them with an explanation.

This case happened in a recreational area in the US, a fact which helps to explain the concerns expressed by local people!

ADAPTING THE UNIT

☐ Many students need help with reading and interpreting the tables and figures.

☐ The unit works well as a group discussion activity. Arrange students in small groups and give them Part 1. (It saves time if they have had a homework in which to read through it.)

Allow about 20 minutes for discussion and then arrange a reporting back session before handing out Part 2 (individual work).

☐ A shorter approach is to give each group one of the four laboratory reports to consider and report back, followed by a class discussion and Part 2.

☐ The unit has been used as a holiday project.

☐ The BBC Radio programme, 'The Water Pollution Mystery', is about the purification of drinking water, rather than the problem of dissolved gases. As such, it supports prior work on water purity but does not support the activity itself. It may also be used with the new unit SATIS 1210, *Bottled Water*.

First published 1986

Hypothermia

Science content

Body temperature, blood circulation, heat transfer by conduction convection and radiation.

Science curriculum links
AT3   Processes of life
AT13 Energy

Syllabus links
- GCSE Science, Biology, Physics
- Sixth-form General Studies
- Technology

Cross-curricular themes
- Health Education

Lesson time
1 hour or more

Links with other SATIS materials
404   How would you Survive?
BBC Radio SATIS Topics 14–16
    Hypothermia
NERIS
Search on
    HYPOTHERMIA

STUDENT ACTIVITIES

☐ Reading and answering questions: hypothermia, treatment of.

☐ Reading and applying learning to case studies: old people, hikers.

USE

As extension work in biological topics on health and body maintenance and in physics to show applications of heat transfer to human situations (especially Parts 2 and 3).

In technology it can be used as a starting point to present design opportunities, for example, in textiles to design a garment to reduce the risk of hypothermia.

ADAPTING THE UNIT

☐ The BBC Radio programme, 'Hypothermia', supports this unit with a visit to a premature baby unit and talks to a health visitor who has many elderly patients. It may best be used with Part 2.

☐ May be linked with experimental investigations, plotting cooling curves for a lagged, unlagged and a foil-wrapped can. (Baked bean cans – but check for sharp edges – are much cheaper than beakers suggested in the Teachers' Notes.)

☐ Investigate the cooling of hot water bottles with various coverings.

☐ Get students who go hiking, canoeing, skiing, etc. to talk about the precautions they take to prevent hypothermia.

☐ A 5 minute exercise – describe a situation which could arise in which you might be at risk of hypothermia.

☐ Examine new textiles for outdoor activities.

☐ Collect reports from mountain rescue teams.

☐ Obtain local information and data on elderly people.

First published 1986

The Technology of Toilets

Science content

Sanitation, water management, control by feedback, water pressure.

Science curriculum links

AT 3 Processes of life
AT 5 Human Influences on the Earth

Syllabus links
- GCSE Science, Biology, Physics
- History
- Sixth-form General Studies
- Technology

Cross-curricular themes
- Health Education
- Environment

Lesson time
1 hour
(homework possible)

Links with other SATIS materials
708   Appropriate pumps
304   A Medicine to Control Bilharzia

STUDENT ACTIVITIES

☐ Reading and answering questions: the need for sanitation, historical development, types of toilet, development of the water closet, control of cistern water level, pressure and head of water.

USE

The unit looks at the science involved in the design of an everyday appliance. It links with work in biological topics on disease prevention, water supply and sanitation and in physics with control and pressure.

It is a fun topic for an odd lesson, suitable for all abilities and well-suited for students to tackle on their own.

The unit is written on a gradient of difficulty, with the more difficult concepts towards the end.

Links with work in technology on housing and the built environment.

ADAPTING THE UNIT

☐ Questions 10 to 16 are considerably harder. Less able students could be asked to omit them.

☐ The unit could be extended into a discussion of designs for low water usage WCs (for example, dual flush cisterns and the valve WCs used in caravans, aircraft and boats).

☐ May be extended into a group discussion exercise. *Is waterborne sanitation the best system for countries with a chronic water shortage? Suggest other possibilities.*

First published 1986

Electrostatic Problems

Science content

Electrostatic charge, insulator, conductor, safe discharge, earthing.

Science curriculum links
AT11 Electricity and magnetism

Syllabus links
○ GCSE Science, Physics

Lesson time
1–2 hours

Links with other SATIS materials
1007 240 Volts Can Kill

NERIS
Search on
ELECTROSTATICS

STUDENT ACTIVITIES

☐ Watching demonstrations, reading and answering questions: fire hazards, powders in pipes, earthing, protecting electronic components.

USE

To extend work on electrostatics to show the hazards of a build-up of electrostatic charge in a variety of industries.

The information and demonstrations are suitable for all abilities. Less able students may need help with some of the questions.

FURTHER INFORMATION

Notes on the demonstrations

Although the demonstrations are not inherently dangerous, a safety screen should be used whenever there is a risk of explosion. Paraffin/water mixture cannot be disposed of down the sink. It is suggested that they are allowed to separate, the water removed and the paraffin dried over anhydrous calcium chloride.

☐ Place a sheet of OHP acetate on a metal plate in the dark. Rub and remove. A sheet of 'flame' is seen at the point of separation.

☐ The main failure of modern Van de Graaff machines is due to deposits on the belt which increase its conductivity. If it fails to work, wash it with water and dry in warm air.

☐ The custard powder bomb. The pressure developed is much lower than in a hydrogen/air explosion. However, teachers should have due regard to safety.

☐ Powders in pipes. This experiment needs to be done with as large a funnel and can as possible. Detection of charge with an electroscope is unimpressive. If the room is darkened, a fluorescent lamp or a neon bulb can be seen to light up.

First published 1986

The Search for the Magic Bullet

Science content

Use of medicines, chemotherapy, azo dyes, syphilis, sulphonamide drugs.

Science curriculum links
AT3   Processes of life
AT17 The nature of science

Syllabus links
○   GCSE Science, Biology

Cross-curricular themes
○   Health Education

Lesson time
    1–2 hours
    (homework possible)

Links with other SATIS materials
305   A Medicine to Control Bilharzia
        – Part 2
309   Microbes make Human Insulin
510   Perkin's Mauve
609   Hitting the Target

NERIS
Search on
        KOCH R

STUDENT ACTIVITIES

☐ Reading and answering questions: identification of anthrax, tuberculosis, cholera, chemotherapy and disease.

☐ Making a time-chart of the discovery of medicines.

USE

To link with work in biological topics on the discovery of medicines and the treatment of diseases.

First published 1986

Stress

Science content

Stress, physiological reactions, health.

Science curriculum links
AT 3 Processes of life

Syllabus links
  o GCSE Science, Biology
  o Sixth-form General Studies

Cross-curricular themes
  o Health Education

Lesson time
    1–2 hours

Links with other SATIS materials
203   Drinking Alcohol
503   Paying for the National Health
603   The Heart Pacemaker
1005 Mental Illness

BBC Radio SATIS Topics 14–16
    Stress

NERIS
Search on
        PSYCHOLOGICAL STRESS or
        STRESS MANAGEMENT
or on
        MENTAL HEALTH

STUDENT ACTIVITIES

☐ Reading and answering questions: a personal stress situation.

☐ Group discussion: six illustrations involving stressful situations.

☐ Reading and answering questions: physiological effects of stress.

☐ Experimental work: pulse rate in stressful situations.

☐ Discussion: symptoms of chronic stress, relieving stress.

USE

To link with work on health, response to stimuli, respiration, circulation of the blood, hormones. Suitable for all abilities. The activities are developed in a sequence to start students thinking about and recognising some of the features of stress.

ADAPTING THE UNIT

☐ The BBC Radio programme, 'Stress', talks to teenagers attending the Harvey Jones Adolescent Unit in Cardiff. It provides useful support to the unit and is best used either to introduce it or to follow-up afterwards.

☐ Create a glossary of terms used in the unit, such as *anxiety, syndrome, physical reaction, chronic tension, phobia, depression.*

First published 1986

SATIS

Radiation – how much do you get? No. 807

Radiation – how much do you get?

Science content

Radioactive decay, energy transfer, biological effects, dose.

Science curriculum links

AT1 Exploration of science
AT4 Genetics and evolution
AT8 Explaining how materials behave
AT13 Energy

Syllabus links
- GCSE Science, Physics
- Sixth-form General Studies
- A-level Physics

Cross-curricular themes
- Health Education
- Citizenship

Lesson time
2 hours
(homework possible)

Links with other SATIS materials
109 Nuclear Power
204 Using Radioactivity
508 Risks
1010 Can it be done?
 (questions 7, 33, 37)
1105 Radon

BBC Radio SATIS Topics 14–16
 Radiation – how much do you get?

SATIS Audiovisual
 Radiation Around Us

NERIS
Search on
 RADIATION and UPPER SECONDARY
or on
 RADIATION MEASUREMENT

STUDENT ACTIVITIES

☐ Reading and answering questions: radiation, dose.

☐ Working out your dose: from sources of radiation on a record sheet supplied.

☐ Translating data into graphical form.

☐ Reading, data interpretation and questions: the risks from radiation.

USE

To extend work on radioactivity and link to effects on health.

This is a difficult unit, suitable for work late in the fifth year or lower sixth (however, some third year use is reported). Generally enjoyed by all, producing some interesting results. Has been used for a staff training day!

ADAPTING THE UNIT

☐ Need not be done in its entirety.

☐ Introduce it in class and finish for homework.

☐ Use with SATIS Audiovisual tape-slide programme, *Radiation Around Us*, to introduce the unit.

☐ The BBC Radio programme supporting this unit visits the Chernobyl area and talks to an environmental health officer who checks background radiation and monitors food. Probably best used to follow-up the unit.

OTHER RESOURCES

The National Radiological Protection Board now produce a free leaflet/poster called *Radiation Doses – Maps and Magnitudes* as well as the more comprehensive booklet, *Living with Radiation*. See the Teachers' Notes.

FURTHER INFORMATION

Since the preparation of the unit, estimates of public exposure to radiation in the UK have been revised. There have also been revisions in the estimates of risk associated with radiation exposure.

First published 1986

TEACHERS' NOTES

Page (ii) *Ground and buildings, paragraph 2* The average dose outdoors is 16 μSv per year. This is because people spend relatively little time outdoors. The average dose rate however, not taking account of occupancy, is in fact about 200 μSv per year. The average dose received indoors is about 340 μSv per year again taking account of occupancy. The total dose from gamma radiation in the UK is on average about 350 μSv per year.

Page (iii) *Radiation from medical treatments* Strictly one should say that the estimated doses from chest and dental X-ray examinations take account of the fact that more than one film may be used.

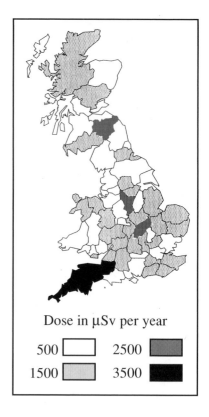

Dose in μSv per year

500 ☐   2500 ▨

1500 ▨   3500 ■

New Figure 4   Radon map of Britain

Please revise the following figures in the unit

Information	Old figures	New figures
Teachers Notes Page (iii)	5, 50	5, 240
Revised table for nuclear power industry	100, 350	220, 250
	200, 840	100, 330
Page 3		
Average dose at sea level in the UK	240 μSv per year	250 μSv per year
Page 4		
Map	Figure 4	New map for fig. 4
Radiation from food and drink	370 μSv per year	300 μSv per year
Page 5		
Radiation from nuclear power	2 μSv per year	1 μSv per year
Living near Sellafield	1000 μSv per year	330 μSv per year
Page 6		
Ash from coal	4 μSv per year	0.2 μSv per year
Page 7		
Low level radiation	2200 μSv per year	2500 μSv per year
Why is it hard to be sure?		
Risk	1 in 100 000	1 in 20 000
Deaths from cancer	1200	5000
Total cancer deaths per year	145 000	160 000
Page 8		
Table 2		
Natural causes for a 40-year-old adult	1 in 850	1 in 700
Radiation dose at a rate of 1000 μSv per year	1 in 80 000	1 in 20 000

Nuclear Fusion

© ASE 1991

Science content

Energy resources, fossil fuels, nuclear fuels, renewable energy sources, fusion, atom, nucleus, isotope.

Science curriculum links

AT8 Explaining how materials behave

AT13 Energy

Syllabus links

○ GCSE Science, Physics

○ Sixth-form General Studies

○ A-level Physics

Lesson time

1 hour

(plus homework)

Links with other SATIS materials

109 Nuclear Power

403 Britain's Energy Sources

601 Electricity on Demand

NERIS

Search on

NUCLEAR FUSION

or on

NUCLEAR POWER and

ELECTRIC POWER

GENERATION

STUDENT ACTIVITIES

☐ Reading and preparing for structured discussion: energy sources for the future, fusion power station, nuclear fusion.

☐ Test on nuclear fusion.

☐ Structured discussion: briefings for a chairperson and four 'experts'.

USE

As extension work on energy sources and on nuclear physics. An exciting unit, describing the frontiers of nuclear research. More suitable for able students in the fifth or sixth years.

ADAPTING THE UNIT

☐ Use the first 4 pages as far as the test.

☐ An alternative is to share out the briefing sheets and have students deliver mini-lectures on them.

FURTHER INFORMATION

By July 1990, the JET Project had achieved plasma temperatures up to 300 million degrees and in individual experiments (but not simultaneously) reached energy confinement times and plasma densities sufficient for a reactor. These are the best results obtained anywhere in the world.

The results enable a next step reactor to be designed that will produce a fully self-sustaining plasma. The fusion reaction will create enough energy from the α-particles to keep the plasma hot enough for further fusion reactions to continue, whilst the energy of the neutrons so produced will be converted into electrical power.

JET is scheduled to close at the end of 1992, but there is a proposal before the Council of Ministers to extend some work until 1996.

Americans, Russians, Japanese and Western Europeans are designing the experimental reactor to follow JET. It will be called ITER (International Thermonuclear Experimental Reactor) and the design team is based in Germany alongside the European equivalent next step device called NET (Next European Torus).

First published 1986

Ball Games

Science content

Mass, volume, elastic energy, friction, air resistance.

Science curriculum links
AT1   Exploration of science
AT10 Forces
AT13 Energy

Syllabus links
○ GCSE Science, Physics
○ Physical Education

Lesson time
    1–2 hours

Links with other SATIS materials
705   Physics in Playgrounds

NERIS
Search on
    PHYSICS and SPORTS

STUDENT ACTIVITIES

☐ Reading and answering questions: ball games, exercise and health.

☐ Activity: finding the diameter, mass, volume of balls and identifying the material.

☐ Experiment: comparing the bounce.

☐ Investigation and questions to answer: design a fair test to find factors which affect the flight of balls.

USE

Extension work on frictional forces, motion, kinetic and potential energy. Suitable for all abilities. The unit provides opportunities for assessment of experimental skills.

ADAPTING THE UNIT

☐ May be used in parts.

☐ The Teachers' Notes contain many suggestions for further experimental investigations.

First published 1986

High Pressure Chemistry

Science content

Haber process, catalysis, gas temperature–pressure relationship.

Science curriculum links

AT7   Making new materials

AT17 The nature of science

Syllabus links
  ○   GCSE Science, Chemistry

Lesson time
      ³/₄ **hour**
      (or homework)

Links with other SATIS materials
207   The Story of Fritz Haber

NERIS
Search on
        HABER PROCESS

STUDENT ACTIVITIES

☐ Reading and answering questions: Carl Bosch, manufacture of chemicals at high pressure, designing a reactor vessel, catalysts.

USE

To extend work on ammonia and the Haber Process and illustrate some of the problems of chemical engineering.

A short unit which is suitable for able students. It assumes prior knowledge of the Haber Process.

ADAPTING THE UNIT

☐ Students may find it helpful to make a glossary of some of the terms used, for example, *fixing nitrogen, reactor vessel, catalyst, brittle, diffuse.*

First published 1986

The Chinese Cancer Detectives

Science content

Life style and health: cell division, cancer, nutrition and food preservation.

Science curriculum links
AT3   Processes of life
AT17 The nature of science

Syllabus links
○ GCSE Science, Biology
○ Geography
○ Sixth-form General Studies
○ A-level Biology

Cross-curricular themes
○ Health Education

Lesson time
1 hour
(plus homework)

Links with other SATIS materials
110   Hilltop – an agricultural problem
509   Homoeopathy
1002 Quintonal

NERIS
Search on
CANCER or CARCINOGENS

STUDENT ACTIVITIES

☐ Reading and answering questions: cancer, carcinogens.

☐ Reading a case study and questions: high rate of cancer cases in Lin Xian valley.

☐ Role-play: four role cards to discuss what should be done to help people in the valley.

USE

As extension work on cells and diseases, to develop information handling and communication skills. Better suited to middle or upper abilities and sixth-form biology or general studies.

A good example of a human problem without a single solution.

ADAPTING THE UNIT

☐ Students may find it helpful to produce a glossary of the technical words used in the unit, such as, *tumour, benign, malignant, metastasis, carcinogen, gullet.*

First published 1986

Acid Rain

Science content

Acid rain, pH, oxides of sulphur and nitrogen, environmental impact.

Science curriculum links

AT 5 Human Influences on the Earth

Syllabus links

○ GCSE Science, Biology, Chemistry,
○ Geography
○ Sixth-form General Studies

Cross-curricular themes

○ Environment

Lesson time

1–2 hours

Links with other SATIS materials

301 Air Pollution
1103 Save the Salmon

SATIS Audiovisual

Acid from the Air

NERIS

Search on
ACID RAIN and UPPER SECONDARY
or on
POLLUTANT GASES and SULPHUR DIOXIDE

STUDENT ACTIVITIES

The unit is a structured discussion exercise.

☐ Reading: sources of acid rain, its effects.

☐ Doing a test: 10 quick questions.

☐ Preparation for the structured discussion: briefing sheets for a chairperson and four 'experts'.

☐ Discussion.

USE

Links with work on using fossil fuels and environmental pollution, with acidity and with ecosystems.

The SATIS audiovisual tape-slide pack, although not essential, provides a good introduction. The tape-recorded commentary gives more details than the General Briefing. It may be used along with the General Briefing.

Students need about 25 minutes for the group discussion itself.

This has been a very popular unit with fourth and fifth-year groups of upper and mixed ability.

ADAPTING THE UNIT

It has been found that the discussion needs an end point such as:

☐ a brief presentation to the class from each group using an OHP transparency,

☐ a set of proposals suggesting what individual citizens can do to reduce acid rain.

FURTHER INFORMATION

Acid rain is a major environmental problem across Europe, parts of Canada and the US.

Since the unit was written

☐ Unleaded petrol is now taxed so that it costs less to buy than leaded (although it is more expensive to make). (Please correct this point on EB2.)

☐ Catalytic converters are now fitted to some cars in the UK. They increase fuel consumption slightly. Catalytic converters are not yet mandatory in the UK.

☐ Production of sulphur dioxide in Britain has fallen slightly. The British Government is committed to cutting down sulphur

---

First published 1986

dioxide emissions but not all power stations will be fitted with flue gas desulphurization scrubbers.

☐ The Central Electricity Generating Board has been divided into four companies. The use of flue gas desulphurization is under way with the largest power stations being fitted first. British coal is high in sulphur. If low sulphur coal were imported, expensive equipment to remove sulphur dioxide from flue gases would not be necessary.

NEW MATERIAL

An optional extra page, GB 3 with the relevant chemical equations.

Production of sulphur dioxide in Western Europe in 1989 (million tonnes)	
Britain	3.8
West Germany	1.5
East Germany	4.4
Italy	2.4
France	1.5
Spain	3.3

SATIS No. 902 Acid Rain   GB 3

The main causes of acid rain are:

sulphur dioxide, SO_2,
sulphur trioxide, SO_3,
nitrogen monoxide, NO,
nitrogen dioxide, NO_2.

These oxides react with air and water to make acids. There are many different chemical reactions that happen in the air.

Sulphur dioxide does not react directly with oxygen in the air. The formation of sulphuric acid from sulphur dioxide occurs via a highly complex system of reactions involving other pollutants as well as oxygen.

The most important reactions are:

1   Sulphur dioxide reacts with nitrogen dioxide to make sulphur trioxide and nitrogen monoxide.

$$SO_2(g) + NO_2(g) \longrightarrow SO_3(g) + NO(g)$$

2   Sulphur trioxide reacts with water to make sulphuric acid.

$$SO_3(g) + H_2O(l) \longrightarrow H_2SO_4(aq)$$

3   Nitrogen monoxide reacts with oxygen to form nitrogen dioxide again. This can then take part in reaction 1 again.

$$2NO(g) + O_2(g) \longrightarrow 2NO_2(g)$$

4   Burning fuels also produce oxides of nitrogen. Oxygen and nitrogen combine at the high temperatures inside an engine or furnace. Fossil fuel power stations and motor vehicles are major producers.

$$N_2(g) + O_2(g) \longrightarrow 2NO(g)$$

What are the Sounds of Music?

Science content

Music, noise, waveform, pitch, loudness, tone, harmonic series, sound synthesis.

Science curriculum links
AT14 Sound and music

Syllabus links
○ GCSE Science, Physics

Lesson time
    1–3 hours
    (homework possible)

Links with other SATIS materials
407   Noise

BBC Radio SATIS Topics 14–16
    What are the Sounds of
    Music?

NERIS
Search on
    PHYSICS and MUSIC
or
    MUSICAL INSTRUMENTS

STUDENT ACTIVITIES

☐ Reading and answering questions:

   – Part 1   Distinguishing musical sounds from noise.

   – Part 2   How string and wind instruments produce musical sounds.

   – Part 3   How synthesizers make and shape musical notes.

☐ Experimenting:

   – Part 4   Observing or carrying out simple demonstrations on the science of musical sound.

USE

As introductory or extension work on sound and music. Suitable for most abilities.

ADAPTING THE UNIT

☐ The BBC Radio programme, 'What are the Sounds of Music?', provides examples of the musical sounds mentioned in the unit. It is best listened to with the relevant part of the unit.

☐ Part 4 Investigations (1 hour). Could be used separately. Enjoyable for less able students.

☐ Parts 1 and 2 (1 hour) Questions are structured for independent work. May be used for homework.

☐ Part 3 (1/2 hour) is suitable for more able students.

OTHER RESOURCES

☐ *'Physics Education'*, volume 25 No. 1, January 1990. This edition features seven articles for teachers on the theme of physics and music and provides background information to the unit.

☐ BBC TV 'Science in Action, Good vibrations'.

First published 1988

Which Bleach?

Science content

Bleach, sodium hypochlorite, chlorine.

Science curriculum links
AT 1   Exploration of science
AT 7   Making new materials

Syllabus links
○   GCSE Science, Chemistry
○   A-level Chemistry

Cross-curricular themes
○   Health Education
○   Economic Awareness

Lesson time
    2 hours
    (plus homework)

Links with other SATIS materials
307   Chemicals from Salt
709   Which Anti-acid?

STUDENT ACTIVITIES

☐   Reading and answering questions: uses of bleach, safety.

☐   Planning an investigation into value for money.

☐   Measuring the strength of bleach.

☐   Calculations and discussion.

USE

Links with work on chlorine, alkalis and measurement skills. Develops awareness of safety precautions in handling a household chemical.

The experiment is suitable for Key Stage 4 only when conducted under close supervision. As the Teachers' Notes suggest, some teachers may prefer to dilute the bleach in advance. Undiluted bleach is very corrosive. The ASE's *Topics in Safety*, 1988 edition, includes chlorates(I) (hypochlorites) in the list of restricted chemicals. Students at Key Stage 4 (but not younger) can use undiluted bleach, but only under close supervision. Younger students may use diluted bleach (less than 1% available chlorine), but again close supervision is required.

ADAPTING THE UNIT

☐   Finding the end point is easier, if after adding a drop of blue ink, a small drop of the mixture is put onto filter paper. The filter paper method detects the first trace of blue and gives the student a coloured record of the experiment.

FURTHER INFORMATION

☐   Chlorine-free bleaches, based on hydrogen peroxide, are now marketed as environment-friendly.

First published 1988

The Impact of Information Technology

Science content

Information technology and transmission, implications for everyday life.

Science curriculum links
AT12 IT including microelectronics

Syllabus links
- GCSE Science, Physics
- Technology
- Sixth-form General Studies

Cross-curricular themes
- Careers
- Citizenship
- Economic Awareness

Lesson time
    1–2 hours
    (homework possible)

Links with other SATIS materials
306   Fibre Optics and
        Telecommunications
507   Computers and Jobs
610   Robots at Work
906   IT in Greenhouses
1010   Can it be done?
        (questions 22, 25, 32, 41)

NERIS
Search on
       INFORMATION
       TECHNOLOGY and
       TECHNOLOGICAL ADVANCEMENT
or on
       INFORMATION
       TECHNOLOGY and
       NEW TECHNOLOGY

STUDENT ACTIVITIES

☐ Reading and answering questions: about IT, areas of impact.

☐ Discussion points suitable for small group work.

☐ Group analysis exercise.

USE

To extend work on microelectronics to its social and economic implications.

The unit has been used in sixth-form general studies, but should now be valuable for Key Stage 4.

ADAPTING THE UNIT

☐ A spokesperson may present the outcome of each group's discussion to the class.

First published 1988

IT in Greenhouses

Science content

Plant growth, control by feedback, implications of control technology.

Science curriculum links
AT2   The variety of life
AT12 IT including microelectronics

Syllabus links
- GCSE Science, Biology
- Sixth-form General Studies
- Technology

Lesson time
      1–2 hours

Links with other SATIS materials
507   Computers and Jobs
905   The Impact of Information
      Technology

NERIS
Search on
      GREENHOUSES and
      COMPUTERISED CONTROL

STUDENT ACTIVITIES

☐ Reading and answering questions: the inputs to a greenhouse environment – sunlight, humidity, carbon dioxide, temperature and water in the soil.

☐ Problem-solving: control problems facing the grower, sequencing the steps for automatic control of carbon dioxide.

☐ Reading and answering questions: an integrated control system.

USE

As an extension to work on monitoring and control of systems, to show the scientific and commercial application of such a system.

Suitable for all abilities. May be linked with practical work. The information presents opportunities for students to design water- and light-sensing control systems.

FURTHER INFORMATION

☐ The example is simplified (as the Teachers' Notes say). The purpose of shading is to reduce transmission of the far infrared which causes the temperature rise. Growers need as much light as possible to promote growth. Control of temperature is achieved by both ventilation and shading.

☐ There is a close relationship between plant water requirement and solar radiation. With less sunlight, less water is transpired. In fact, plants close their stomata at night, when carbon dioxide levels are high and when they have insufficient water.

First published 1988

Your Stars – Revelation or Reassurance?

Science content

Testing predictions, the use of evidence and the tentative nature of proof.

Science curriculum links
AT1 Exploration of science
AT17 The nature of science

Syllabus links
○ GCSE Science, Physics
○ Sixth-form General Studies

Lesson time
1–2 hours

Links with other SATIS materials
509   Homoeopathy

BBC Radio SATIS Topics 14–16
Your Stars – Revelation or
Reassurance?

STUDENT ACTIVITIES

☐ Reading and answering questions: the difference between astronomy and astrology.

☐ Reading and answering questions: examples of predictions e.g. meteorological, planetary orbits, risk analysis, etc.

☐ Testing predictions: spinning a coin, random number generation.

☐ Testing predictions: horoscopes, birth signs.

USE

A stimulating exercise about making predictions and about the nature of science.

Very enjoyable, but the latter parts are not for low ability students.

ADAPTING THE UNIT

☐ The BBC Radio programme, 'Your Stars – Revelation or Reassurance', talks to Joan Quigley, Mrs Reagan's astrologer, and Nigel Henbest, a scientist. Best used along with Part 3 on horoscopes. Students could be asked to write down the arguments the programme makes for and against astrology.

☐ Less able students would find Part 1 taken alone a short and satisfactory exercise.

First published 1988

Why not Combined Heat and Power?

Science content

Energy, power, efficiency.

Science curriculum links
AT11 Electricity and magnetism
AT13 Energy

Syllabus links
- ○ GCSE Science, Physics
- ○ Sixth-form General Studies
- ○ A-level Physics

Cross-curricular themes
- ○ Economic Awareness

Lesson time
    1–2 hours
    (homework possible)

Links with other SATIS materials
308   The Second Law of – What?
403   Britain's Energy Sources
601   Electricity on Demand

NERIS
Search on
    ELECTRIC POWER
    GENERATION and ENERGY
    CONSERVATION

STUDENT ACTIVITIES

Reading, doing calculations and answering questions:

    Part 1 Defining power and efficiency,

    Part 2 Combined heat and power stations,

    Part 3 District heating,

    Part 4 The economics of CHP with district heating.

USE

The concept of efficiency is the main theme. Use as extension and revision work on energy and the generation and distribution of electricity.

This is a difficult unit packed with interesting calculations which will tax the stamina of able fifth formers and well-motivated lower-sixth physicists. The ideas behind the unit are important and it is worth extracting parts of it for average students.

ADAPTING THE UNIT

☐ Average students can usefully tackle pages 2 and 3. For a new question 1, they could redraw Figures 2 and 3 with 'boxes' for the power stations and show energy inputs and outputs with arrows. This should help with answering question 2.

FURTHER INFORMATION

☐ The unit does not discuss small scale CHP systems which can supply heating and electricity to single home or a group of homes. A study by the Open University Energy Research Group showed that a system producing 40 kW of electricity could heat 50 houses and save money.

☐ Denmark has almost halved its use of fossil fuels for heating by adopting CHP stations which have an overall efficiency of 85 per cent.

☐ Teachers' Notes (ii) Q.7 Delete paragraph two. (The problem of costing CHP plant has changed. With effect from 1 April 1990 the rate payable on all generating stations over 0.5 MW will be the same.)

First published 1988

Aids

Science content

AIDS, disease, the immune system, sexual intercourse.

Science curriculum links
AT 3   Processes of life

Syllabus links
○   GCSE Science, Biology
○   Sixth-form General Studies

Cross-curricular themes
○   Health Education

Lesson time
        1–2 hours

Links with other SATIS materials
503   Paying for the National Health
1010   Can it be done?
          (question 35)

NERIS
Search on
        AIDS

STUDENT ACTIVITIES

☐   Quiz: a true/false test on AIDS.

☐   Group discussion: case studies of people with AIDS.

☐   Reading: information about AIDS.

USE

The unit should be used within the guidelines of the School Governors' policy on sex education.

Links with work on disease or on the blood.

Suitable for all abilities. Best done in class.

ADAPTING THE UNIT

☐   If time is limited, parts of the unit may be used separately.

FURTHER INFORMATION

☐   *Student page 1, question 11*. Most people who get AIDS now die within 3 years. (However, survival times are still improving.)

☐   *Factsheet 5*. Wearing a condom during intercourse cuts down the risk of infection with *HIV and other sexually transmitted diseases*.

☐   In 1990, 1 in 4 babies born in New York USA was HIV positive. AIDS has not spread to the heterosexual population as rapidly as was initially forecast, however evidence suggests that the number of cases in the UK is now growing exponentially.

First published 1988

Disposable Nappies

Science content

Polymers and uses of materials.

Science curriculum links
AT 1 Exploration of science
AT 6 Types and uses of materials

Syllabus links
○ GCSE Science, Chemistry
○ Sixth-form General Studies

Cross-curricular themes
○ Health Education

Lesson time
   2 hours
   (plus homework)

Links with other SATIS materials
709   Which Anti-acid?
904   Which Bleach?

STUDENT ACTIVITIES

☐ Reading and answering questions (may be done for homework): about disposable nappies.

☐ Data interpretation decision-making exercise: selecting materials for nappies.

☐ Practical work: plan and carry out a comparison of nappies.

☐ Reading and answering questions: further information on the structure of disposable nappies, disposal, manufacture.

USE

As extension work on materials, recycling, in parentcraft lessons. Suitable for all abilities, particularly the 'fair test' section in Part 3.

ADAPTING THE UNIT

☐ Part 3, comparing nappies may be used as a design and test exercise.

First published 1988

Chocolate Chip Mining

Science content

Extraction of minerals, metals in the Earth's crust, copper mining.

Science curriculum links
AT 1 Exploration of science
AT 5 Human Influences on the Earth
AT 7 Making new materials

Syllabus links
○ GCSE Science, Chemistry
○ Geography

Cross-curricular themes
○ Environment
○ Economic Awareness

Lesson time
1–2 hours

Links with other SATIS materials
602 The Limestone Inquiry
604 Metals as Resources
1203 Prospecting by Chemistry

NERIS
Search on
COPPER MINING
or on
METALLIFEROUS
MATERIALS

STUDENT ACTIVITIES

☐ Practical work: simulation of mineral extraction – extracting chocolate chips from cookies.

☐ Reading, data management and answering questions: minerals, copper extraction.

USE

Links with work on metals or on using the Earth's resources.

Part 1, the practical work, is suitable for all abilities. Part 2 is more demanding.

ADAPTING THE UNIT

☐ Select questions carefully for less able students.

☐ A money-saving suggestion: 'I put talcum powder on the biscuits to stop the kids eating them.'

☐ Some students try to dissolve out the biscuit from the chocolate chips. Beware of blocked sinks!

First published 1988

Quintonal – an industrial hazard

Science content

Cancer, carcinogens, cells.

Science curriculum links
AT 3 Processes of life

Syllabus links
○ GCSE Science, Biology,
   Chemistry
○ Sixth-form General Studies

Cross-curricular themes
○ Health Education
○ Citizenship

Lesson time
   1–2 hours
   (homework possible)

Links with other SATIS materials
508   Risks
904   The Chinese Cancer Detectives

NERIS
Search on
        CANCER
or
        CARCINOGENS

STUDENT ACTIVITIES

☐ Reading information (preparation for role-play, may be done for homework): cancer, treatment of cancer, causes, industrial cancers.

☐ Role-play: eight roles.

USE

May be used to link with work on health and disease and to develop awareness of industrial safety.

Suitable for students of average ability and above.

ADAPTING THE UNIT

☐ The general briefing contains no active learning. Some questions are provided in the new material.

☐ A 'local newspaper report' and a 'journal article' are provided in the new material to brief students on the 'situation' at Wilsons.

☐ Some teachers find there are too many roles for their students to cope with. An alternative is to select some of the roles and run the role-play as a small group exercise, with a spokesperson reporting back to the class at the end.

Strategy 1. *Suggestions for a five role discussion* – shop steward (role 2), company safety officer (role 3), local GP (role 4), company nurse (role 5), consultant industrial chemist (role 7).

Strategy 2. *Two types of discussion group – the 'outsiders' and the 'insiders'* which would produce different perspectives to report back to the class.

Insiders – managing director (role 1), shop steward (role 2), company safety officer (role 3), company nurse (role 5).

Outsiders – local GP (role 4), local councillor (role 6), consultant industrial chemist (role 7), local tenants representative (role 8).

NEW MATERIAL

Questions relating to the general briefing and stimulus material for the discussion.

First published 1988

Questions about the general briefing

Q1   *What has gone wrong with cells in a cancer?*

Q2   *Name two types of cancer.*

Q3   *How do secondary growths start?*

Q4   *Why is it important to detect a cancer at an early stage?*

Q5   *What sort of treatments may be recommended for a cancer?*

Q6   *What is a carcinogen?*

Q7   *It often takes many years before a substance is discovered to be carcinogenic. Explain why this is. (For example, asbestos was used as a building material for many years. It is now recognised as a carcinogen.)*

Is there anything to worry about at Wilsons?

Wilsons Plastics Company is a well-respected local firm. Two articles have been drawn to your attention. One is from the local paper, the other appeared in an American medical journal. They both mention a chemical called quintonal. Wilsons use quintonal in the manufacturing process but no trace remains on the finished product.

Your task is to discuss these articles. But instead of giving your own opinions, you will be given a role to play. Read the articles and your role card carefully. Make notes of the points you would like to make in the discussion.

FAREWELL TO DON AND RON

Two well known local figures died this week. Was it fate that made Don Smith and Ron Downs pass away from the same disease on the same day? They had been best friends for over forty years.

Don and Ron became pals at school. When they left, they both went to work for Wilsons Plastics Company.

Their widows, Pat and Betty, claim the cancers were more than a coincidence. Although Ron left Wilsons Plastic Company five years ago, Pat and Betty recall both coming home with the smell of quintonal on their clothing. They wonder if it caused the bladder cancers from which their husbands died.

A spokesperson for Wilsons Plastics Company said that quintonal had been used in the manufacturing process for the past 10 years. There was no evidence of any adverse effects on human health.

IS QUINTONAL A CARCINOGEN?

Dr Armit, speaking at a press conference in the US, said that several cases of bladder cancer had been reported among workers in plastics factories in Canada and the US.

The workers who died had been in contact with a chemical called quintonal.

Research scientists have found that when rats are given large doses of quintonal, 80% develop bladder cancer.

Dr Armit said the evidence gave cause for concern, but more research was needed. He added that if quintonal were a cause of bladder cancers, the risk to workers was much lower than that of smoking.

A Big Bang

Science content

Combustion, fuels, hazardous chemicals.

Science curriculum links
AT 7 Making new materials

Syllabus links
○ GCSE Science, Chemistry
○ Sixth-form General Studies

Cross-curricular themes
○ Citizenship

Lesson time
1–2 hours
(homework possible)

STUDENT ACTIVITIES

This is a decision-making exercise.

☐ Reading: the scenario – the warehouse storing chemicals.

☐ Reading and information handling: the evidence.

☐ Deciding on an explanation (working in small groups).

☐ Making recommendations: what could be done to stop it happening again.

☐ Writing an article.

USE

As extension work on fuels, the fire triangle and oxidation. The unit will fit logically into many parts of the syllabus. It puts students in the position of 'investigators' of the incident. Suitable for all abilities.

'A very motivating unit – thoroughly enjoyed!'

ADAPTING THE UNIT

☐ Less able students can be helped to assimilate the information in the text, if the evidence is read aloud by 'actors' – one student taking the part of a Factory Inspector and calling upon the six witness (pages 2 and 3) to give their evidence.

First published 1988

Lavender

Science content

Horticulture, selective breeding and economic benefits, separating and purifying techniques, symbolic representation of molecules.

Science curriculum links
AT 1 Exploration of science
AT 2 The variety of life
AT 4 Genetics and evolution
AT 7 Making new materials
AT 8 Explaining how materials behave

Syllabus links
○ GCSE Science, Biology, Chemistry
○ A-level Biology

Cross-curricular themes
○ Economic Awareness

Lesson time
1 hour or more
(plus homework)

Links with other SATIS materials
510   Perkin's Mauve

STUDENT ACTIVITIES

☐ Observing a teacher demonstration: steam distillation of lavender, putting together a cut and stick diagram of the apparatus.

☐ Reading, drawing conclusions from data and answering questions: the best conditions for growing lavender.

☐ Cut out a diagram, answer questions: the perfume molecules in lavender.

☐ Reading and answering questions: breeding lavender hybrids.

☐ Reading and answering questions: the lavender business.

USE

This is an interdisciplinary unit which will link with several science syllabuses. It may be used to extend work on soil, horticulture or on selective breeding. The chemical aspects relate to steam distillation and to the use of structural formulas.

Parts may be used to adapt it for all abilities. Has also been used in A-level biology.

Safety advice Both students and the teacher should wear eye protection. The boiler must not be allowed to boil dry, but should not be so full that it boils over. Teachers should be vigilant over the possibilities of blockages occurring in the narrower tubes.

Mental Illness

Science content

Mental health, neurosis, psychosis.

Science curriculum links
AT 3 Processes of life

Syllabus links
○ GCSE Science, Biology
○ Sixth-form General Studies

Cross-curricular themes
○ Health Education
○ Citizenship

Lesson time
1–2 hours

Links with other SATIS materials
503 Paying for National Health
806 Stress

NERIS
Search on
MENTAL DISORDERS

STUDENT ACTIVITIES

☐ Reading and answering questions: what is mental illness, who gets it, types of mental problems, causes, treatment.

☐ Group discussion questions.

USE

Links with work on health, emotional changes, stress and drug abuse.

Suitable for middle and upper ability groups and for sixth formers. May be used in association with SATIS 806 *Stress*.

First published 1988

As Safe as Houses

Science content

Energy conservation, conduction, convection, radiation, structure, strength and materials, survival and climate.

Science curriculum links
AT10 Forces
AT13 Energy

Syllabus links
○ GCSE Science, Biology, Physics
○ Technology

Lesson time
1–2 hours
(homework possible)

Links with other SATIS materials
106 The Design Game
404 How Would You Survive?
1009 Trees as Structures

NERIS
Search on
CONSTRUCTION MATERIALS
and BUILDINGS

STUDENT ACTIVITIES

☐ A building survey: materials, structures, safety features.

☐ Reading, data handling and questions: timber frame and wet construction, strength, density and thermal conductivity of building materials.

☐ Information handling: data on window frame materials.

☐ Reading and answering questions: adaptation to environment, building techniques.

USE

As part of work on the properties of materials, forces and energy in science and technology or to link with heat transference in physics.

The unit may be linked with the study of buildings in local history and with work on the built environment in technology.

Parts of the unit are suitable for all abilities, the physics is for average students and above.

ADAPTING THE UNIT

☐ The unit may be used in the order pages 5, 6, 7, 8, which are conceptually easy and suitable for independent study, then page 1 (the survey) and lastly pages 2, 3 and 4 which contain the more demanding concepts.

OTHER RESOURCES

☐ *Architecture in Education* is a resource book of over 200 classroom projects, including ideas for modelling forces in structures using the students themselves! It may be obtained by sending a cheque for $25 payable to 'Foundation for Architecture' (British cheques can be written in $ though they may take some time to clear, or send travellers cheques.) Post to The Foundation for Architecture, Suite 1665, One Penn Center at Suburban Station, Philadelphia, PA 19103, USA. (Previous orders have been fulfilled very quickly!)

☐ The Timber Research and Development Association produce material for all age groups: Richard White, Education Officer, Stocking Lane, Hughenden Valley, High Wycombe, Bucks HP14 4ND.

First published 1988

240 Volts can Kill

Science content

Voltage, electrical resistance, current, fuses, residual, current device, life saving.

Science curriculum links
AT1   Exploration of science
AT11   Electricity and magnetism

Syllabus links
○   GCSE Science, Physics
○   A-level Physics

Cross-curricular themes
○   Health Education

Lesson time
1–2 hours
(homework possible)

Links with other SATIS materials
701   Electricity in Your Home
1008   Why 240 Volts?

SATIS 16–19
3   Do we need a Europlug?
71   Plug into safety

STUDENT ACTIVITIES

☐   Experiment: measuring body resistance.

☐   Reading, calculations and questions: body resistance and current, why shocks are dangerous, fuses, RCDs.

USE

Links with work on using mains electricity. To do the calculations, students should be familiar with the relationship between p.d., current and resistance.

Suitable for middle and upper abilities. However, this is an important topic and parts of the unit may be used with lower ability students.

ADAPTING THE UNIT

☐   The experiment is suitable for lower ability students. Questions need to be selected carefully. They may be better tackled by small group discussion. Questions suggested: 1, 2, 7, 8, 9, 11, 14.

☐   Adapt Figure 3 for a multicultural society, which may have English as a second language – no words to be used.

FURTHER INFORMATION

☐   Students might wish to know that an ohm meter contains a battery which sends a small current through the objects whose resistance is being measured. It assumes Ohm's Law to give a value of the resistance.

☐   Students should note that people may have wet skin (and therefore a lower resistance) in kitchens as well as bathrooms. (Teachers Notes i, bottom of the page, and Q.7 on page 2.)

☐   Q.10 and Q.11. A fuse cannot save one from electrocution.

☐   Figure 6 has a non-linear scale (students are not required to read it).

☐   Misspelling – Teachers' Notes iii should say *Kirchhoff* on the first line.

First published 1988

Why 240 Volts?

Science content

Mains electricity supply, power, voltage and current, energy efficiency.

Science curriculum links
AT1   Exploration of science
AT11 Electricity and magnetism

Syllabus links
○ GCSE Science, Physics
○ A-level Physics

Lesson time
1–2 hours
(homework possible)

Links with other SATIS materials
701   Electricity in Your Home
704   Electric Lights
1007 240 Volts can Kill

SATIS 16–19
25   Why 50 Hz?

STUDENT ACTIVITIES

☐ Reading, calculations and answering questions: history of choice of 240 volt supply, calculations involving power current and voltage.

☐ Experimental investigation: voltage and efficiency of light bulbs.

USE

As part of work on domestic energy use, for practice in substitution in the *power = current × voltage* formula.

The conceptual level and mathematical demands make the unit better suited to average ability and above.

The investigation is excellent for developing understanding of the power–p.d. relationship, and, surprisingly, is not a traditional physics experiment.

ADAPTING THE UNIT

☐ The diagrams on page i of the Teachers' Notes could be given to more able students.

☐ If used in the lower sixth, the investigation can lead to a discussion of the relationships which derive from the equations in this unit and SATIS 1007:

$$P = \frac{V^2}{R} \qquad\qquad P = I^2 R$$

First published 1988

Trees as Structures

Science content

Adaptation to environment, structure size and strength, forces, turning force, wind resistance.

Science curriculum links
AT1   Exploration of science
AT2   The variety of life
AT10 Forces

Syllabus links
○   GCSE Science, Biology, Physics

Lesson time
    1–2 hours

Links with other SATIS materials
501   Bridges
1006   As Safe as Houses
1106   Tin Cans

STUDENT ACTIVITIES

☐ Reading, drawing to scale, pattern finding by plotting data and answering questions: the problem of being big.

☐ Experimental investigation, pattern finding: tree design.

USE

Links to work on adaptation to environment, structure and forces, moment of a force.

The unit looks at how the structure of trees fulfils their function as solar collectors.

For the experimental work, check that the dowelling is sufficiently flexible to give reasonable displacements with the masses supplied. Alternative materials would be small plant stakes or bamboo canes. Students may need to cramp the stands or weight them down to stop them toppling. This is a problem they ought to anticipate and solve for themselves. Have G cramps or spare kilogram masses to hand!

OTHER RESOURCES

☐ *On size and life*, by Thomas A McMahon and John Tyler Bonner, Scientific American Library (1983), ISBN 0 7167 5000 7, is a fascinating book written by a biologist and an engineer which develops such ideas further.

☐ Forestry Commission, Public Information Division, 231 Corstorphine Road, Edinburgh EH12 7AH. Catalogue available.

First published 1988

SATIS

Can it be done? Should it be done? No. 1010

Can it be done? Should it be done?

Science curriculum links
ATs 2–16

Syllabus links
○ GCSE Science, Biology,
  Chemistry, Physics
○ Sixth-form General Studies
○ Technology

Cross-curricular themes
○ Health Education
○ Environment
○ Economic Awareness

Lesson time
½ **hour or more**

Links with other SATIS materials
See references on units

BBC Radio SATIS Topics 14–16
Can it be done? Should it be
done?

STUDENT ACTIVITIES

☐ Responding to a set of suggestions: scientific developments –
are they possible, should they be attempted?

USE

Use as thought-provoking material to stimulate discussion into
the social, environmental, technological applications and
implications of scientific developments.

The unit may be used as it stands, or some of the questions
considered in relation to other SATIS units.

ADAPTING THE UNIT

☐ There are several suggestions in the Teachers' Notes.

☐ The BBC Radio programme supporting this unit, takes the
development of the supersonic aircraft, Concorde, as a case
study and considers whether a new plane should be built. The
programme could be used as an introduction to this unit.

First published 1988